D1497925

Within the Stone

Best wishes to Julia,

Bill Atkinson

August 3, 2004

Oh granite, finite

vaults of ingenious rock,

come ignite my eyes.

Diane Ackerman

WITHIN THE STONE

PHOTOGRAPHY BY BILL ATKINSON

ROCK DESCRIPTIONS BY

SI & ANN FRAZIER
ROBERT HUTCHINSON

POETRY AND ESSAYS BY

DIANE ACKERMAN
LAURA ATKINSON
PHILIP BALL
JOHN HORGAN
ANDREW REVKIN
DORION SAGAN
TYLER VOLK
DAVID ZINDELL

BROWNTROUT PUBLISHERS
2004

Within the Stone: Nature's Abstract Rock Art
Photography by Bill Atkinson

Entire Contents © 2004 BrownTrout Publishers, Inc.
Photography © 2004 Bill Atkinson
Text © 2004 Bill Atkinson
Text © 2004 Diane Ackerman (pp. 24, 34, 36, 46, 110, 118, 124, 132, 138, 148)
Text © 2004 Laura Atkinson (p. 154)
Text © 2004 Philip Ball (pp. 16, 22, 44, 64, 66, 68, 78, 82, 94, 108)
Text © 2004 John Horgan (pp. 26, 30, 38, 56, 62, 112, 120, 130, 136, 150)
Text © 2004 Robert Hutchinson (p. 104)
Text © 2004 Andrew Revkin (pp. 20, 54, 58, 70, 74, 76, 86, 102, 106, 142)
Text © 2004 Dorion Sagan (pp. 14, 32, 40, 52, 90, 116, 128, 140, 144, 152)
Text © 2004 Tyler Volk (pp. 12, 18, 50, 72, 80, 84, 88, 92, 98, 100)
Text © 2004 David Zindell (pp. 28, 42, 48, 60, 96, 114, 122, 126, 134, 146)

All rights reserved under International and Pan-American Copyright Conventions.
No part of this book may be reproduced, stored in a retrieval system, or transmitted,
in any form or by any means, electronic, mechanical, photocopying, recording, or otherwise,
without prior permission in writing from the publisher.

Library of Congress Cataloging-in-Publication Data

Atkinson, Bill, 1951-
  Within the stone : nature's abstract rock art / Photography by Bill Atkinson ;
commentary by Si & Ann Frazier and Robert Hutchinson ; poetry and essays by Diane
Ackerman … [et al.].
    p. cm.
  ISBN 0-7631-8189-7 (alk. paper)
 1. Photography in mineralogy. 2. Photography of rocks. 3. Rocks—Pictorial works.
I. Ackerman, Diane. II. Title.
  TR732.5.A88 2004
  779'.3—dc22   2004006729

Published by BrownTrout Publishers, Inc.
P.O. Box 280070, San Francisco, CA 94128-0070 U.S.A.
800-777-7812
www.browntrout.com

Printed and bound by Vanfu, Inc., Japan

Contents

List of Plates

ESSAYISTS

DIANE ACKERMAN, poet and science writer, has written *An Alchemy of the Mind, A Natural History of the Senses, Origami Bridges, Jaguar of Sweet Laughter,* and many other books of natural history, essays, and poetry. She has won the John Burroughs Award and the Art of Fact Award and hosted a five-hour PBS television series based on her book, *A Natural History of the Senses.* She is professor of humanities at Cornell University. The organic molecule *dianeackerone* is named after her.

PHILIP BALL, science writer and dramatist, has written *Bright Earth: Art and the Invention of Color, Designing the Molecular World, The Self-Made Tapestry, Critical Mass, H₂O,* and several one-man plays. He is physical sciences editor of *Nature* and a regular contributor. He has won the Association of American Publishers Award and the Association of British Science Writers Award, and he was shortlisted for a National Book Critics Circle Award. His book *I Am Different: The Life and Legacy of Paracelsus* grew out of one his plays, *Paracelsus the Great.* He is writer-in-residence in the chemistry department of University College, London.

JOHN HORGAN, science writer and philosopher, has written *The End of Science, The Undiscovered Mind,* and *Rational Mysticism.* He has twice received the Science Journalism Award of the American Association for the Advancement of Science, as well as the Science-in-Society Award of the National Association of Science Writers and the American Psychiatric Association's Certificate of Commendation.

ANDREW REVKIN, science writer and musician, has written *The Burning Season* and *Global Warming.* He is the environmental science reporter for *The New York Times.* He has won the Sidney Hillman Foundation Book Prize, the Robert F. Kennedy Book Award, a National Academy Communication Award, two Science Journalism Awards of the American Association for the Advancement of Science, and has shared in a Pulitzer Prize. He is an adjunct professor at the Columbia School of Journalism. Two Hollywood movies, *The Burning Season* and *Rock Star,* have been adapted from his writing. He is a musician and songwriter, often performing with Pete Seeger.

DORION SAGAN, science writer and novelist, has written or co-written *Biospheres, Microcosmos, Origins of Sex, Acquiring Genomes, Up From Dragons,* and *Garden of Microbial Delights.*

TYLER VOLK, science writer and anthropologist, has written *Metapatterns Across Space, Time, and Mind* and *Gaia's Body.* He is associate professor of biology in the Earth Systems Group at New York University. He was formerly a biologist for NASA and taught architecture at the School of Visual Arts and Cooper Union.

DAVID ZINDELL, science fiction writer and mathematician, has written *Lightstone, Neverness,* and other novels.

Within the Stone features seventy-two color photographs of polished sections of natural rock specimens, most of them cryptocrystalline or colloidal silicas such as jasper, agate, and opal. All seventy-two images are detailed macro photographs taken by reflected light. The photographer and digital printmaker is Bill Atkinson, the neuroscientist/computer scientist/artist who designed much of the original Macintosh user interface and developed a superior method of digital printmaking.

Seventy of the photographs were divided into sets of ten and submitted to seven writers, each distinguished—like the photographer—by bimodal professional accomplishments in both the sciences and the arts. Each writer was invited to participate in a game with the following rules. He or she was to respond reflexively to each of his or her ten assigned photographs according to his or her trained sensibility and to record those responses in ten essays written in quasi-automatic fashion. The form and substance of each essay was to be entirely ad libitum, according to the taste and discretion of the writer: whether prose or poetry; whether in an aesthetic, psychological, philosophical, poetic, scientific, literary, or otherwise idiosyncratic vein. No research effort was expected or desired—the more unmediated and impromptu the response, the better. Each writer was encouraged to write in a variety of registers. Finally, each writer was promised that no essay would be altered in any way for publication.

Every one of the seven players reported afterward that she or he had found the game psychologically gripping and creatively rewarding. Several players said that they had succumbed to the game almost obsessively, returning to certain photographs again and again seeking to resolve indistinct shapes in the penumbra between remembered dream and forgotten memory that seemed to cast their shadows on the scrim of the image. Several players expressed an inclination to keep playing the game on their own, to continue mapping in words the terrain of deep memory and primitive ideation within the stone images. One player, speaking to a conference of psychoanalysts, recommended the therapeutic use of images from *Within the Stone* as Rorschach patterns for people in the arts.

When the seven sets of essays were compared, it became apparent that each essayist—working in isolation from the other essayists and without editorial prompting—had written on themes that were harmonically related to themes in the essays of the others. In some cases, several writers hit upon remarkably similar responses to quite dissimilar stones; in other cases, quite dissimilar responses to similar stones. The whole corpus of essays displayed a sort of shimmering unity, not unlike the effect of one of Atkinson's photographs.

Robert Hutchinson

PHOTOGRAPHER'S PREFACE

WHILE PHOTOGRAPHING the Arizona landscape in the Petrified Forest National Park, I encountered, in a riverbed, several pieces of petrified wood that had been cracked, and then polished by flowing water. The exposed colors and shapes were captivating. Wanting to see more, I visited several nearby rock shops and purchased a number of beautiful cut and polished pieces of petrified wood.

I brought these polished rocks back home to my studio, studied them to find expressive compositions, and carefully photographed them under glare-free lighting. The resulting photographs were exciting and evocative—even more so than the original rocks.

The photographs looked like abstract paintings. Their shapes and colors showed a timeless mystery and complexity, such that each image kept revealing new secrets. Abstracted from the rocks, the images showed no sense of scale and provided fertile ground for imagination and wonder.

As I showed the photographs to people, I found that different people saw different things within them, but almost no one saw them as flat polished rocks. The rock photographs were like colored Rorschach tests, encouraging each person to project his or her own personal experiences onto the images.

I sought out more polished rocks to photograph, buying or borrowing and photographing a wide variety of rocks in addition to the petrified wood, and I refined my techniques for photographing them.

For higher resolution and more accurate color than possible with film, I switched from my Hasselblad medium-format film camera to a BetterLight large-format scanning digital camera.

I researched lighting technologies and assembled custom high-intensity lighting fixtures which would allow me to use polarized lighting with the new camera. I found that these bright lights and glare-blocking filters revealed more intricate details and brought out the colors more intensely than one would see on casual examination by room light.

The large, fine-art prints that I made of these rock images were well received in public exhibitions and in the galleries that sell my work, but I wanted to share these images with a much wider audience, in the form of an art book.

To find more rocks to photograph, I began attending the annual Tucson Gem and Mineral Show, where thousands of collectors bring rocks from all around the world. Each year, I packed my car full of photographic equipment, drove to Arizona, and set up a professional photo studio in a motel room. I examined thousands of polished rocks, and purchased and photographed quite a few.

I even bought a diamond-bladed rock saw, a diamond-wheeled bench grinder, and a vibrating flat lap, and learned how to cut and polish rocks myself. However, most of the rocks photographed for this book were already cut and polished by someone else.

At the Tucson Show, I showed a prototype of the book I was making to rock collectors and dealers, and asked permission to borrow their best pieces to photograph in my motel room. Some of them took prized specimens out of their display cases, telling me that they were not for sale but that I could borrow them to photograph. Thanks to their trust and generosity, I have been able to assemble an extensive collection of beautiful rock art photographs.

Over the years as I kept returning to Tucson, I developed friendships with many dealers and collectors. In general, these rockhounds are a warm-hearted and friendly group whose shared passion for rocks brings them from all over the world to gather in Tucson.

They taught me much about rocks and minerals, and generously shared their special techniques to help me as I was learning to polish rocks myself. Over dinner and beers they brought me fascinating stories of life from very different parts of the world.

Every year I delivered a number of large matted and signed fine-art prints to thank those who had allowed me to photograph their rocks the previous year. These were gratefully accepted and cherished and helped to deepen friendships and open more doors for me.

Word spread about me and my book project, and often when I first approached dealers asking to borrow an expensive rock, they would say that friends had already told them about me, and that I could be trusted. More than once a dealer has held an extraordinary specimen for me to photograph before it sold.

Out of the tens of thousands of rocks that I have examined and the thousands that I have photographed, I have chosen my own personal favorite rock images to share in this book.

Each photograph is a work of discovered art that begins with the oldest art form, a natural sculpture created in stone millions of years ago, which has only recently been cut and polished to reveal its inner colors and shapes. Within these colors and shapes, I have searched for evocative and memorable compositions, captured these images with my cameras, and fine-tuned the results to create expressive photographic prints.

As an artist, I have come to believe that beauty is not out there waiting to be discovered. Rather, beauty is created by the human act of noticing and appreciating. I feel that my primary task as an artist is to notice and to appreciate, and only then to share my experience with others.

It is my hope that this book will touch the sensibilities of many people, just as the magnificence in these rocks has touched mine.

Bill Atkinson

STONESCAPES

A Drive for Deep Time

Driving to an appointment in Flagstaff, Arizona, I could hardly afford to detour. But only a few miles east lay more than two hundred million years back in time, at the Petrified Forest National Park, beckoning. Soon I walked among ancient expanses of toppled trunks. These trees, by the gift of mineralization, had voyaged from their own deep time up into our era. Then was an age when strange conifer forests rose to heights that would have felt familiar, yet no flowers adorned the land. Then was an age when the earliest bipedal dinosaurs had just evolved into the fastest and nastiest of runners, while ferret-like mammals were still reptilian works-in-progress.

Far, far in the future came the humans, with tools, language, bloody battles, creation myths—all extensions of a refined drive for survival inherited from ancient creatures, not only those that lived hundreds of millions of years ago but even from the dawn of life. We ask questions: Who are we and how did we get here? To answer, we imbibe history, gaze through telescopes, craft precision instruments that help in untangling facts from stone. And as we begin, in part, to truly reach bottom for those bottomless questions, the lid is lifted for our imaginations.

Tyler Volk

PETRIFIED WOOD

In thin sections some of the oldest known Earth rocks, the cherts of Warrawoona in Western Australia, laid down billions of years ago, when you were just small, we find what look like microspheres, the primal scene of our ancestors caught in the asexual act. Whether or not they were microbes petrified in flagrante delicto (presuming the act was pleasurable for them, or it), or were just inorganic little balls, like the magnetite-containing miniatures of Mars, which nonetheless justified press conferences galore (such is the nature of hope), those triple-billion-year-old babies do not compare, visually, to what we see here. I don't know about you, but I see a candy planet, some secret sister of a Saturnian moon, her green-streaked metaforms, her ices and atmosphere, providing the medium for the growth of blue-green goobies. But let us not jest over the impressive multiplication, from the placenta of pure thought, from the orbicular jasper of Madagascar, of ill-born rings, cross-sections of the infinite. Let us keep an eye on those peacock eyes. Let us watch the watchers.

Lasso the rhinestone cowboy.

Dorion Sagan

TIME

OCEAN JASPER

In the pre-digital age, school children carried booklets filled with numbers. These were logarithmic tables, which turned multiplication and division into addition and subtraction. Either you understood logs or you didn't; many didn't. There was a whiff of numerology in this business of turning numbers into other numbers, in these cryptograms that transform 5 into 0.69897. It hardly seemed an intuitive way to do math.

Yet we do have an intuition of the logarithmic scale. It is how we experience time. There is some kind of subjective equivalence between our sense of yesterday, last week, last month, last year and the past decade of our lives. The recent past is stretched, the distant past compressed, as on a logarithmic measuring stick. The unit of recent history is the year; by the nineteenth century it is the decade. The Roman Empire is marked out in centuries, the Paleolithic in millennia. Geologists continue this compression with units reaching to gigayears: a billion years.

How strange, then, to see a record of individual years in the Triassic period, when a complete annual cycle now seems like nothing, an instant, a shutter-click in deep time, too fast for anything to have happened at all.

Philip Ball

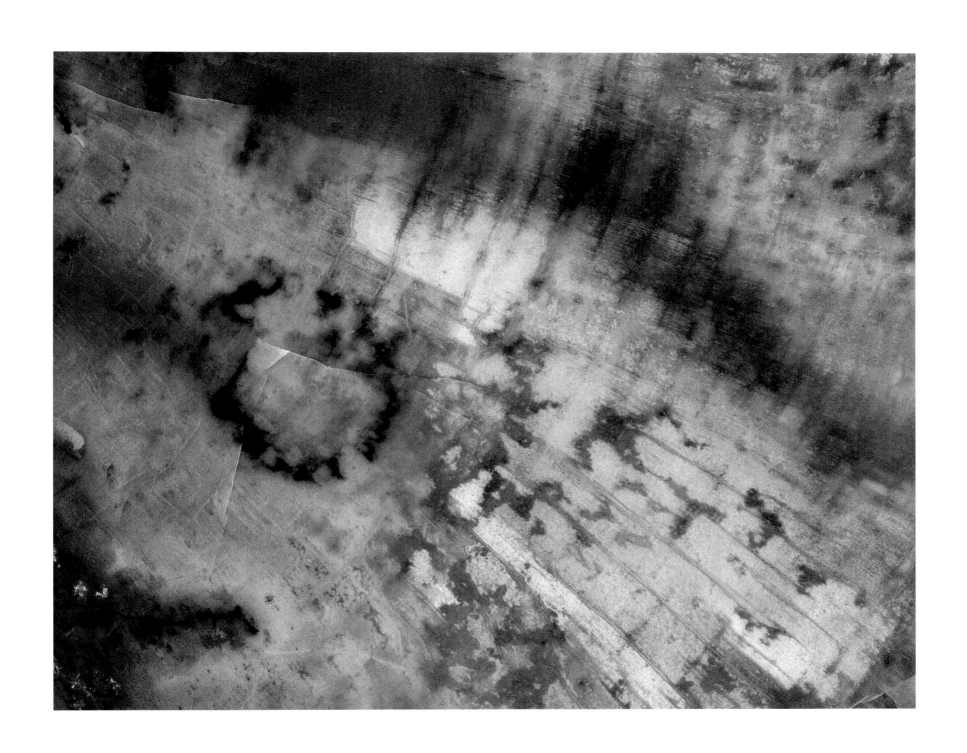

PETRIFIED WOOD

The Unbound Now

The "now" is a wave, a duration of being in time. In physics, a moment can be arbitrarily small—a nanosecond or less. Not so in psychology. Experiments that test visual perception, by varying the interval between a pair of light flashes, point to a minimum of a hundredth of a second for the wave of our being. Other tests (using visual illusions) indicate a more extended period, say a few seconds, as a moving window for the overall context of consciousness, an encompassing wave that contains levels of smaller ones.

Certainly one should take care not to engulf the present moment with obsessions about future or past. Yet our human essence is much tied to our ability to weave a web across the remembered past and the anticipated future, establishing a larger self that rolls beneath the smallest moments like the ocean beneath its swells. Indeed, the minimal interval of perception is too brief a pulse for the brain to discern reality de novo *each time. Even the shortest now contains reverberations from the series of waves in its immediate past, echoes from which shape the now by a continuous flow of prophecy. Echoes and projections even extend from childhood depths to the hopes and dreams of weeks and years ahead. Thus the now is not bound. We spread off the edges of any conceived page.*

Tyler Volk

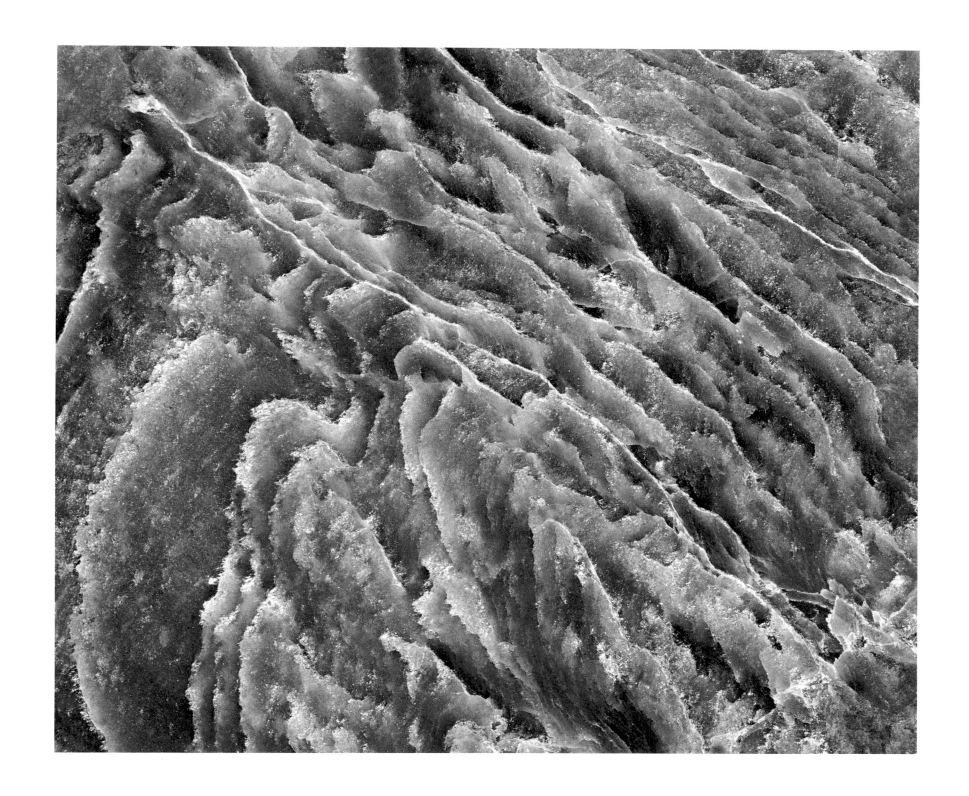

FUCHSITE

*We tend to recognize and give weight to agents of change mainly
if they operate within our frame of reference, an attention span
calibrated to the rhythms of human life—to hours and days,
maybe years, rarely decades.*

*Waves are no such thing. They are fed by forces as near perpetual
as the sun's rays and the Earth's spin. They know nothing of time,
despite their metronomic manner. They roll until impeded.*

*It is the waves that break when surging seas collide with rocky shores.
Thus is born the impression that water is weak and rock a bastion.*

*But it is the human eye, of course, that is weak. Handicapped, really.
Shortsighted in the most profound way.*

Andrew Revkin

TIME

PIETERSITE

The harder we look for simplicity, the further it recedes. It's tempting, sometimes, to suspect that the universe is mocking us. If physicists ever find a unified Theory of Everything, only a handful of them will be able to understand it—that's how simple it is. And if from such a theory everything else follows only out of necessity, couldn't the Creator have devised an easier Great Equation? What was wrong with the ancient model, an earth-centred universe surrounded by eternal heavens, except that reality didn't fit it? Failing this, couldn't the cosmos of Copernicus and Newton be populated just with atoms and empty space? Yet all we can see, all the stars and planets and galaxies, are just a sideshow next to the invisible, mysterious dark matter that accounts for almost a third of creation. And now we have to make room for dark energy, without which we got along just fine until a few years ago even though it apparently accounts for at least two-thirds of all stuff that exists. Together, dark matter and dark energy conspire to focus the galaxies into thin, frozen filaments that thread their glowing paths through barren cosmic voids of unimaginable desolation.

Philip Ball

FORM

SODALITE

Enigma Variation

As messages go, it's polished, she mused, rolling the rock in hand
and mind again. A quarried artifact molded somewhere in space, it
continued to tang her senses even after decades. She felt elated poring
over its straggly black fissures, could almost taste its honey and acorn
yellows. And yet, after years alone and alive with it, still it wouldn't
unpuzzle as she'd hoped—not that other code breakers had had
better luck. But after so long a vigil, such crafty wooing, well, you'd
think .... Once more, then: what did the "H" mean? The "Y"? The
central "M," thickly charred and floating like a middle initial? The
waxy white and blue—was it squid-ink or cyanide blue? Did she ever
know?

Yes, she thought, somehow all its parts congealed, but how? The black
dashes that appeared and disappeared, seemingly at whim—were
they a simple morse-like code, a fossil beacon? Stitches, half-hidden?
How did so many textures and processes—smeared pollen,
chromosome twigs, syrupy squawks, parrot blue marble—all of it
blend with such fluency?

And how could she retire with this siren code unbroken? A last time,
she tasted the rock here and there with the back of the tongue at the
back of her mind, and then sighing, set it down on its black velvet.
Not all opals flash, she thought, sadly, noting a ping in the matrix
down low where—how could she have missed it?—a small pair of
mineral eyes were staring back.

Diane Ackerman

FORM

DENDRITIC OPALITE

Recycling Images

I once worked at a science magazine renowned for its elegant illustrations. Occasionally, I suspected that the art department was recycling the same image for different articles. The picture itself meant nothing, or too much; like an abstract-impressionist painting, it begged explanatory text. What is it? Take your pick: A Hubble Space Telescope snapshot of a supernova shock wave blowing through a globular cluster on the Milky Way's far border. An infrared image from a Soviet Venera spacecraft of an electrical storm illuminating the sulfuric-acid clouds cloaking Venus. An SR-71 "Blackbird" observation of a 15-kiloton fission device detonating near the Khyber Pass. A photograph of a cross-sectioned plume agate chiseled from Graveyard Point on the Idaho-Oregon border. A positron-emission-tomography scan of the left temporal lobe of a 17-year-old epileptic female seized by a religious vision. Complexity theorists discern deep significance in the recurrence of patterns in wildly disparate realms. Reality, in spite of its seemingly boundless diversity, runs on a limited repertoire of algorithms. That art department may not have recycled images, but the Creator does.

John Horgan

FORM

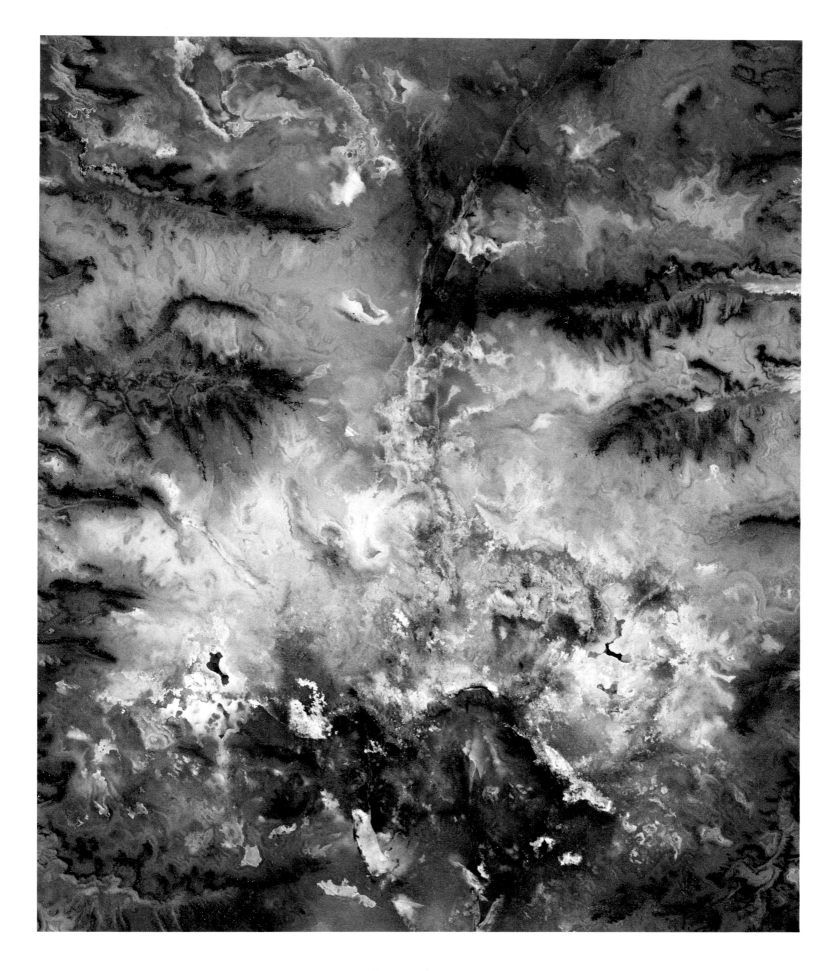

PLUME AGATE

Mathematicians work in their sub-subbranches on the infinite tree
of mathematics proving theorems so arcane that often they can't
explain their discoveries to their fellow professors down the hall. As
the old saw goes, every year they know more and more about less and
less, until someday they'll know everything about nothing. They'll
tell you that a fractal is an infinite iteration across the complex plane,
a mathematical object of self-similarity at all resolutions, such as
the famed Mandelbrot set, generated by: $z_{k+1} = z_k^2 + c$, where c is
a complex number, a + bi, and $z_0 = 0$, and the magnitude of each
successive z remains within a parameter of 2. Gobbledygook. I say
a fractal is God. Look at this photo. It could be glacier ice, as blue as
the sky, but it is stone. Doesn't it pull you down and in? Doesn't it
promise hidden splendors, the shimmering interconnectedness of all
things? Pick any square centimeter. What would it be like to go into
its heart, deeper and deeper, each layer brilliant, perfect and equally
complex? Don't you sense that you would behold more and more
of less and less forever? And at the end of it all, if matter or infinity
could have an end, wouldn't you behold the great Nothing that is
Everything? Isn't this what God is? If you were God, isn't this stone
what you would want: sheer mind-blowing, breathtaking, thank-God-
I'm-alive beauty? God, I say, is a mathematician. God is also this
stone and the one who beholds it.

David Zindell

FORM

BLUE CALCITE

Fractal Free Fall

Mac, my 10-year-old son, comes home from school conveying a classmate's speculations: What if the whole universe is just a germ in the stomach of a giant? And that giant's whole universe is just a germ in an even bigger giant's stomach? And his universe . . .? The old conundrum has him thrilled, a bit anxious: How far up and down does everything go? Scientists, the good ones, never cease to be piqued by our betwixt-and-between predicament. Gazing into deep space, astronomers imagine our cosmos embedded in a vastly larger multiverse consisting of countless worlds, each ruled by its own distinct physics. Giants galore! Looking in the other direction, however, some physicists discern a fundamental increment beyond which no smaller thing exists. This is the Planck scale, 10^{-35} meters, where superstrings supposedly shimmy quarks, protozoans, zebras, nuns, quasars—this whole weird show—into being. Just a guess, of course, a wishful one, meant to ward off the vertigo induced by our apprehension of bottomlessness. The Mandelbrot set, mother of all fractals, may be more apt a metaphor for our plight. Magnify the set's crazy-lace border, and you keep spiraling down into new realms, iterations of the primal pattern, forever. No matter how far you burrow into the heart of things, you never arrive. There is no ground of being.

John Horgan

CRAZY LACE AGATE

Clearly, a galaxy imploded here. The force of its implosion created a
fractal light, a brilliant reminder to porpoises and other sea creatures
that even out of water the stars race, waiting like divine details
in the interstices of the ordinary. Now I say watch the crystalline
granulation fade. Turn the knob up high. You will not see white heat
like this at the bottom of a well without a candle. The flickering is not
just in your mind.

Dorion Sagan

FORM

BOTSWANA AGATE

One Jasper Night

How fast it winters in this archipelago of stars, where Earth lies at anchor, swollen with fidgeting animals and doubloon-like leaves, the scented ooze of flowers, curtseying geese, jasper bays where whales nurse their young, undersea volcanoes in a petrified seethe, whiz-kid machines, and curious herds of humans, who speak, love, muse, squabble, and dream. A meteor storm tonight. On falling stars thick as fireflies, I wish for brawny atmospheric planets small enough to form oceans and harbor life, where other beings, bustling about their chores, may pause to admire the streaming milt of stars. Maybe, like us, they guide by those nomad lights; maybe they've named our lantern. Other worlds, roll gently around your suns tonight. Like you, embedded in the veins of time, we bless you from our palace and thirst of days.

Diane Ackerman

SPACE

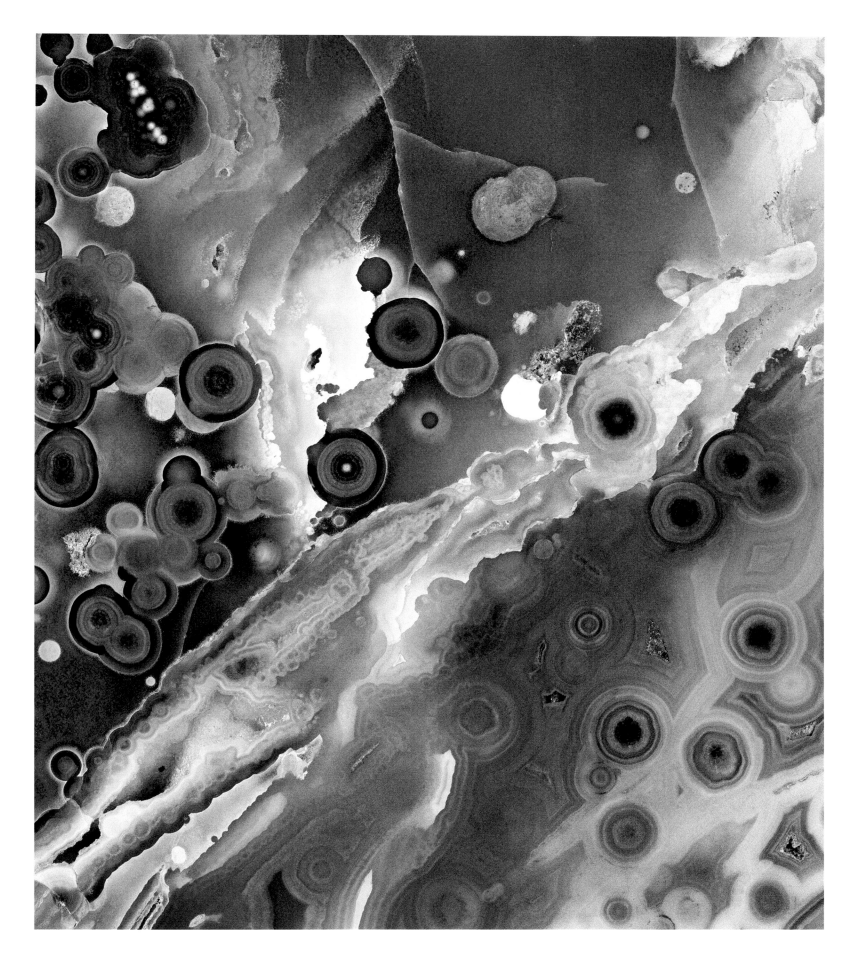

Ocean Jasper

RED-SHIFT

I
Coming and going
I gauge your heat
by how fast you recede,
and where we now lie
in one another's orbit.

The farther we drift
the redder I blush.
The closer we come
the slower time moves.

II
The universe is an endless net
sealed with red jasper
at every knot, each gem
reflecting and reflected in all.

Just as when a flamingo
preens its wings,
and the All, shimmering,
grows visible in every feather,

we orbit each other
as flamingo-red suns,
yet we are only vehicles
of light, not molten stars,
though no less beings
whose beaks rasp
and plush feathers thrill.

Diane Ackerman

SPACE

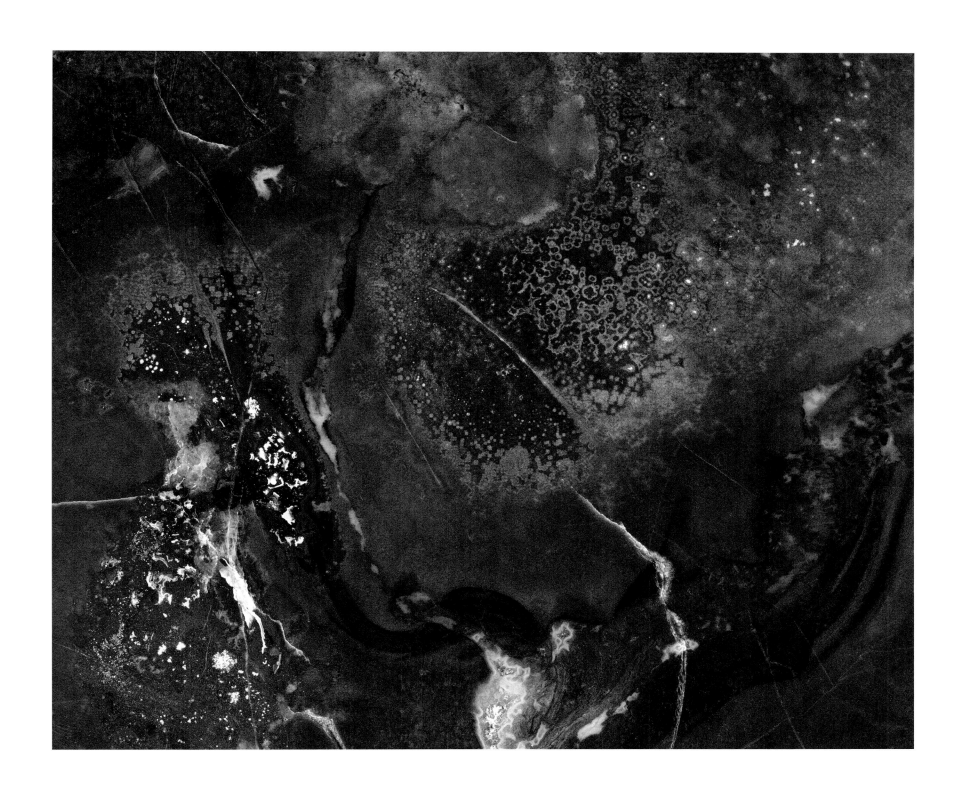

RED JASPER

THE MERMAID OF EUROPA

Are we alone? A once-in-infinity fluke? Or might life exist
elsewhere than on our speck of dirt? We don't know. We may
never know. Our searches have thus far turned up nothing: no
extraterrestrial equivalents of "I Love Lucy" beaming from
Alpha Centauri; no 2001-style monoliths nestled in lunar
craters; no microbes—let alone Venetian metropoli—on Mars.
The extravagantly imaginative physicist Freeman Dyson has not
given up hope. Scanning our solar system for habitable real estate, his
gaze snags on Europa, one of the moons Galileo spied orbiting bloated
Jupiter four centuries ago. Beneath the azure ice encasing Europa,
Dyson conjectures, a liquid ocean moves, warmed by vulcanism
and radioactive decay, teeming with alien marine creatures. In those
deeps, a turquoise-breasted mermaid gliding through aquamarine
rooms turns her bioluminescent eyes toward the cracked, chrysocolla
sky and wonders, Am I alone?

John Horgan

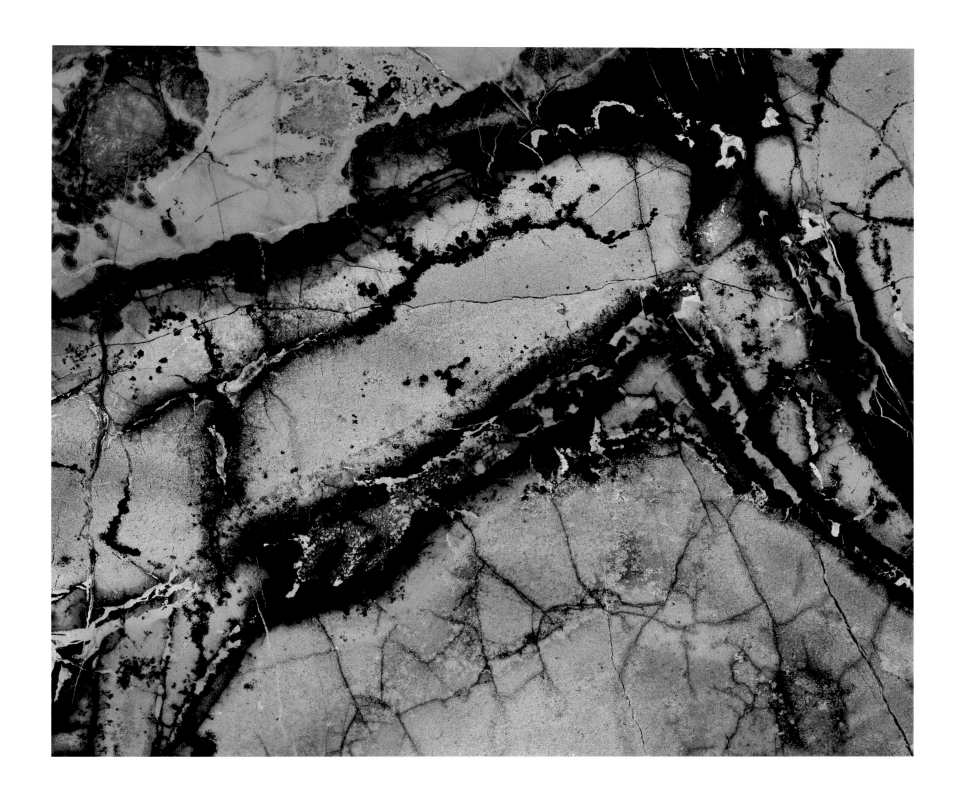

CHRYSOCOLLA

I was working on this novel. It seemed to take up my whole life and even a little more. Here was the part where we looked at Io from the surface of Jupiter, saw the stream of rust where they poured liquid into the shiny mold of new cars. Jasper was our dog, the big poodle who ran around the pool, a spastic incontinent canine that ripped off the pool filter when I tied him to it and never saw how our lives here are like grooves on a record, or that a peach can be more than the sun. Chalk it up to his dog brain. I put an ad in the paper but the lady said I misrepresented him and wanted to give him back. An opaque cryptocrystalline quartz of any of several colors. And I thought it was me. Later I put in the part about the drop of Madagascar vanilla on the clavicle of the edible blonde with the anti-turquoise belt limned in gold, how the naked goddess wanted me to pretend she was a sundae all butterscotch and milk. That used to be my favorite part.

Dorion Sagan

SPACE

Owyhee Picture Jasper

Far, far away in another universe, lives an alien race called the People. They cannot possibly conquer us. If they could come to earth, they couldn't help us, either. The People, in many ways, are much like us. (It doesn't matter what they look like; the souls of all beings are really much the same. Even on earth, dogs are people, too.) They face many of the same problems that we do, and one problem above all: that life lives at the expense of other life. The more successful a people are, the more they devastate other life, and the more they themselves become their own problem.

No matter or energy—or even information—can pass between universes, which are "pinched off" from each other in spacetime. So the People cannot talk to us. But in this little science fiction, with my rules, dreams can pass, for all universes are really one, and this One has a xillion xillion dreams and dreamers but only a single Dream: that life should somehow go on into an infinite future in triumph and glory. The People want us to know this. There is a stone on earth, a chunk of chrysocolla, that looks remarkably like the People's world as seen from space. It reveals both the People's doom and glory. The People want us to dream upon this stone, not in hope of saving us or us saving them, but only so we know that we're not crazy and we're not alone. And in these two things, after all, might be our salvation.

David Zindell

Chiesccolla

I wouldn't go to Mars if you paid me. There are better ways of spending space money than to put people in a can and fire them at the Red Planet. But few better than sending out machines, a bargain even with a 40 percent failure rate. I am always surprised at how emotive the pictures are that they beam back home (and that alone staggers me, like hearing a radio playing in the Marquesas). It's not the strangeness, but rather the opposite. I love a description of the Mars Express *images as 'like an alien landscape'—as though we are not prepared to believe that this is genuinely another world. Mars is strewn with rocks, it has hills and gullies and mountain ranges. Mars has a* sky, *for goodness' sake, I can't get over that. We interpret Martian geology by reference to Earth—aren't those the scablands of Oregon?—like paleontologists rebuilding fossils in the mould of today's bestiary. No wonder we imagine we could live there. But pictures of Mars are heart-wrenching precisely because they are not here, not our home. They show that suns surely rise in salmon-hued glory on the other side of the universe.*

Philip Ball

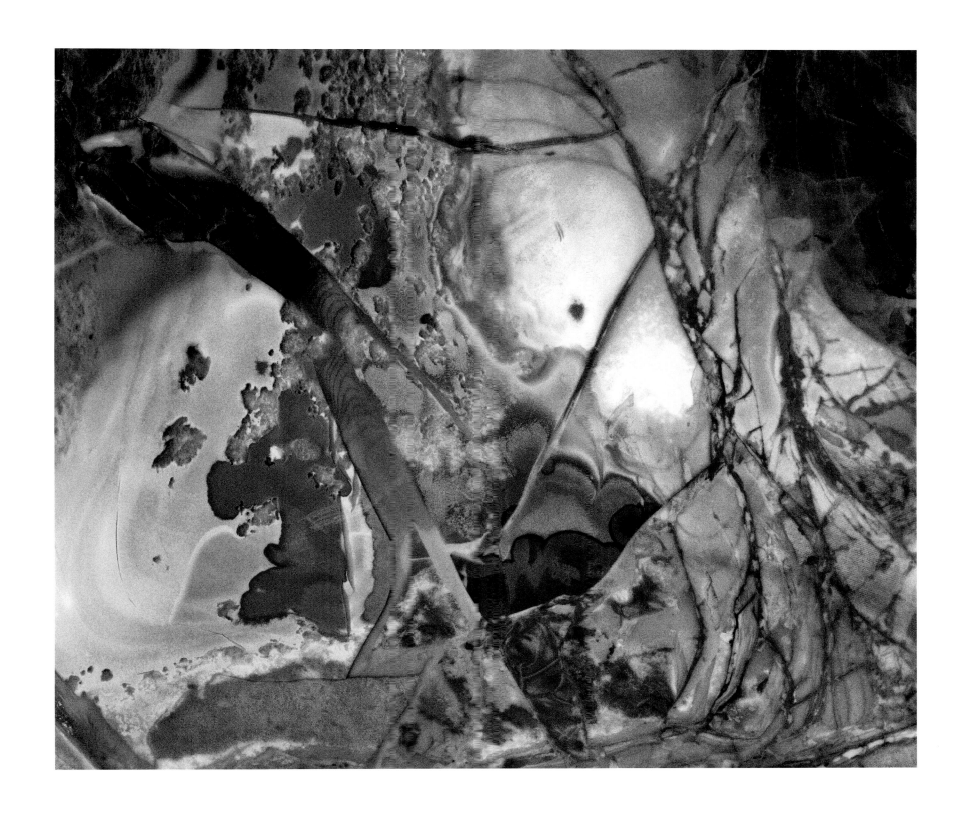

MORRISONITE

PABLO, COME BACK

I long to swim again in our lake
abuzz with water striders
and banjo-plucking frogs
and tall grasses ticking
like metronomes, and small fry
rising to flash in the sun.
I want to float where it's safe
to bathe or mourn,
and practice swinging out
over the water without letting go,
despite gravity, weak arms,
or the yen for release.

Diane Ackerman

Picasso Marble

In a distant land there is a shore of black sands. Amethyst waves crash against it. Those who abstain from the pleasures of the night run here. At sunrise the golden swimmer comes and dives into the waters. As she glides into the waves she hears the sound of her pursuers. She swims hard, out toward the heart of the sea. The waves, here a deep indigo, leap violently around her. The sea roars, urging her forward. Sirens scream and cold buoys chase her. Fear of inhuman captors tears into the swimmer's golden chest and bleeds away her strength. The buoys are mechanized, fast, and they are gaining. Ahead she sees the barrier that separates the beach waters from the open sea. She feels the song of that deep sea and the call of purity. Every muscle of her body strains as she flies through the waves.

When her heart has almost burst, she slows. She is far out now, safe. The ocean around her is all brightness and dark, danger and beauty. The water is fresh and cool on her skin, and she can feel it pulsing with energy. She laughs with joy. Here she is pure, at peace in the waves. She dives down and tickles the spotted fish; she leaps up and calls to a dolphin in the distance. She mimics the sea: as it dances, she dances; as it rises and swells, so does she. Now the whole world is bright purple and radiant. Dawn sunlight bathes the golden swimmer as she floats, far from any shore, in the Charoite sea.

David Zindell

EARTH

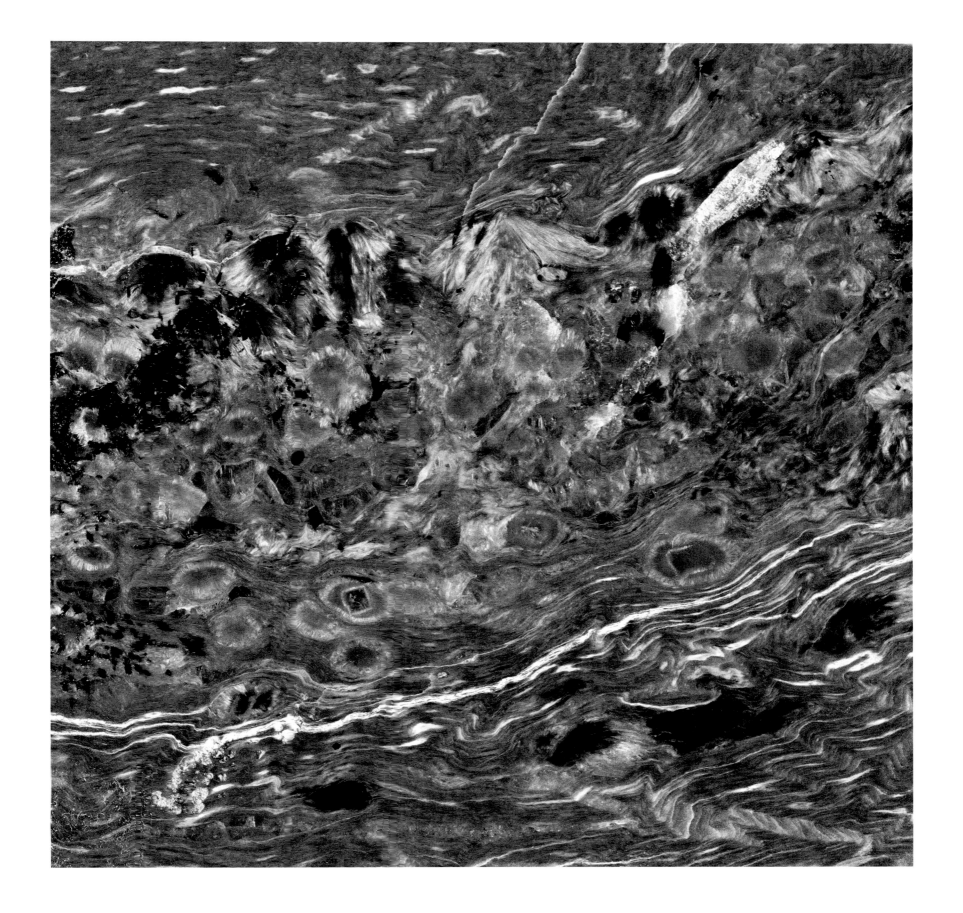

CHAROITE

CAMPSITE

There's a clearing just southeast of center. Well protected by thick forest from the north winds. Shafts between trees where, from a bit north of due east, the summer sun can flood in. To the immediate south, complex islands of brush in which one could get lost for meditation or pure play; places to gather wood for fire. To both east and west, spaces between trees trumpet out into openness, alcoves to sit and enjoy a rich scene or bright bird song. Soothing. Complex. Satisfaction like a full tummy. A hundred pathways for as many days. Mind becomes nature. Broad open expanses all around, fields like circling rivers where one can hail fellow sojourners and watch animals milling at dusk. From large to local, a perfect intermix of open and closed, of order and chaos. That's where I would camp.

Tyler Volk

EARTH

DENDRITIC SOAPSTONE

In this marble lies a petrified forest: of all the trees, all the forests,
enchanted and polluted, black and birch (the white bark tastes
of licorice), tropical palm and frosted New England, glazed and
crunching with eye sugar and crystalline toppings or melting in the
hydrous stalagmite of the white virgin's submission to the seductions
of the sun, whose rays clarify and harden, transforming a solid
to a solid, and ultimately, when he's done with her, to a liquid, in
fairy tales and picture books where little Red Riding Hood wanders
and the Wolf lives, and Rapunzel lets down her golden hair, and
Nabokov's butterflies flutter, their wings marked with simulated
droplets of water that simulate the refraction of blue lines not to
camouflage, hardly, or like eyespots to ward off the predatory bird
(the sun is enough) with a false show of strength, of size, but rather
to let us, at our computers made, like this black-and-blue wood,
mostly of silica, know that there are tricks of smoothness and
disguise we cannot even imagine, barbed-wire worlds flat as the
coffee table glass on which this page may be splayed open, Dante's
hells in a false droplet aloft, a word on a wing over water that is not,
in the Forest of Is.

Dorion Sagan

PICASSO MARBLE

Humanity is etching its signature across its earthscape: diverting waterways, extracting essentials, transforming the air, scratching pathways. The advance is as inexorable, and natural, as that of rust on iron or microbes on a plate of agar. We till that which can be tilled, and therefore must be tilled, until our outward press meets sterile soils. But as we gain a global view, and regard our transformed sphere, we now ponder an unavoidable question: What next?

Andrew Revkin

EARTH

DALI STONE

THE NEVADA TEST SITE

On December 4, 1985, I stood atop a ridge in southern Nevada overlooking a pockmarked wasteland known as Yucca Flat. The scores of craters scarring the desert floor had been formed not by meteors but by nuclear explosions thousands of feet underground. The blast would vaporize the rock, forming a lava-lined cavity that—within a period ranging from minutes to weeks—collapsed, precipitating a thunderous slump at ground level. Later, my tour of the Nevada Test Site took me to Frenchman Flat, where in the 1950s the government tested the effects of open-air bursts on tanks, jets, jeeps, buildings, bunkers, soldiers. A few relics of that era remained: a bridge with girders twisted like licorice sticks, an aluminum bunker squashed as if by a mighty fist. My feelings were, to put it mildly, mixed. Growing up in the duck-and-cover era, I had recurrent nightmares of stumbling alone through a charred, lifeless landscape after the missiles fell. As a proper liberal dove, I also deplored what the Nevada Test Site represented. But part of me wished I could have been there with the soldiers crouching in the trenches, waiting for the apocalyptic fire to bloom in the desert.

John Horgan

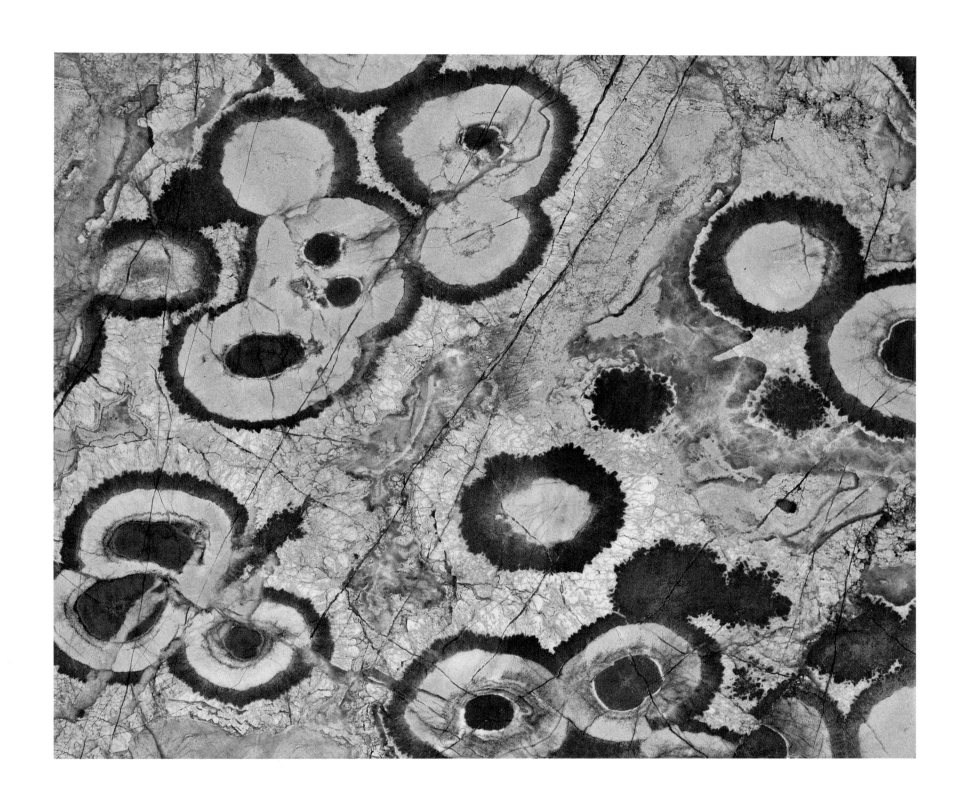

POPPY JASPER

*Layered rock speaks of the ages both in the accumulated strata and
in the way they are exposed after millenniums of scouring by wind
or water eat away at rough outer surfaces.*

*Long ago, while sailing up the Red Sea with others on a small
boat, I felt the antiquity of weathered stone in other ways. Staring
east, we scanned the rounded mountains of the Sinai for meaning,
tracking our progress by matching each successive shape with
silhouettes published in a mariner's guide.*

*Clawing slowly north against dusty gusts, we read the landscape as if
turning the pages of history, marveling at how those same sculptured
forms had guided sailors for a hundred generations or more.*

*Then we sailed through a brief desert shower, which cleared the
air but stained the boat with yellow mud. We were coated in time.
Each wet, wind-blown grain was a tick of God's clock.*

Andrew Revkin

EARTH

BIGGS JASPER

Tibetan lamas make fantastically complex and beautiful sand paintings. In the past, they ground up precious gems such as lapis for blues and rubies for reds to make the sands. Today, they still work painstakingly and with great patience, shaking colored grains out of long bronze tubes called chakpurs *with exquisitely controlled tappings practically grain by grain. They "paint" geometric shapes and spiritual icons arrayed around a great mandala that is meant to be a representation of the universe. Into all these figures, as the sand trickles out and finds its place, hour after hour, day after day, go intention, meditation and prayer. Such paintings might take weeks to complete. But they are not meant to last: nearly as soon as they are finished, the monks pour their paintings into a stream or river, dispersing the sand and letting the water carry their prayers to the world.*

This stone reminds me of a sand painting, but abstract and painted by the earth itself. How long did it take her to crystallize each tiny point and swirl of turquoise, ocher and rose? How long will this stone last before time and erosion inevitably grind it to dust and wash it away? Will the earth, again and again, reassemble its minerals into other stones and other paintings?

The monks pray for peace, understanding, enlightenment, compassion. What, I wonder, does the earth pray for?

David Zindell

EARTH

INDIAN PAINT ROCK

Do Rocks Have Free Will?

The poet Robinson Jeffers, from his Big Sur mountain perch,
saw humanity as a melanoma despoiling Earth's lovely face.
In "November Surf," he envisioned a day when mighty waves
would rise from the Pacific and cleanse the land of this infestation.
These sorts of misanthropic prophecies appealed to me in my cranky
adolescence. As a middle-aged husband and father, I'm still cranky,
but sentimentally inclined to think that in spite and because of all
our faults, nature needs us. Inhuman, nature is merely a magnificent
(perpetual-motion?) machine. Choice, our curse and blessing, infuses
the world with drama. What will we do next? Unleash, perhaps,
some suicidal savagery that leaves the earth to birds and bacteria.
On the other hand, choice may play no role in our destiny. Free will
may be an illusion foisted on us by evolution to keep us from lapsing
into fatalism. Our ebbs and flows, and ultimate fate, may be subject
to laws as deterministic as those that govern Alzheimer plaques
infiltrating a President's hippocampus, or stress fractures riddling a
tectonic plate beneath Baghdad.

John Horgan

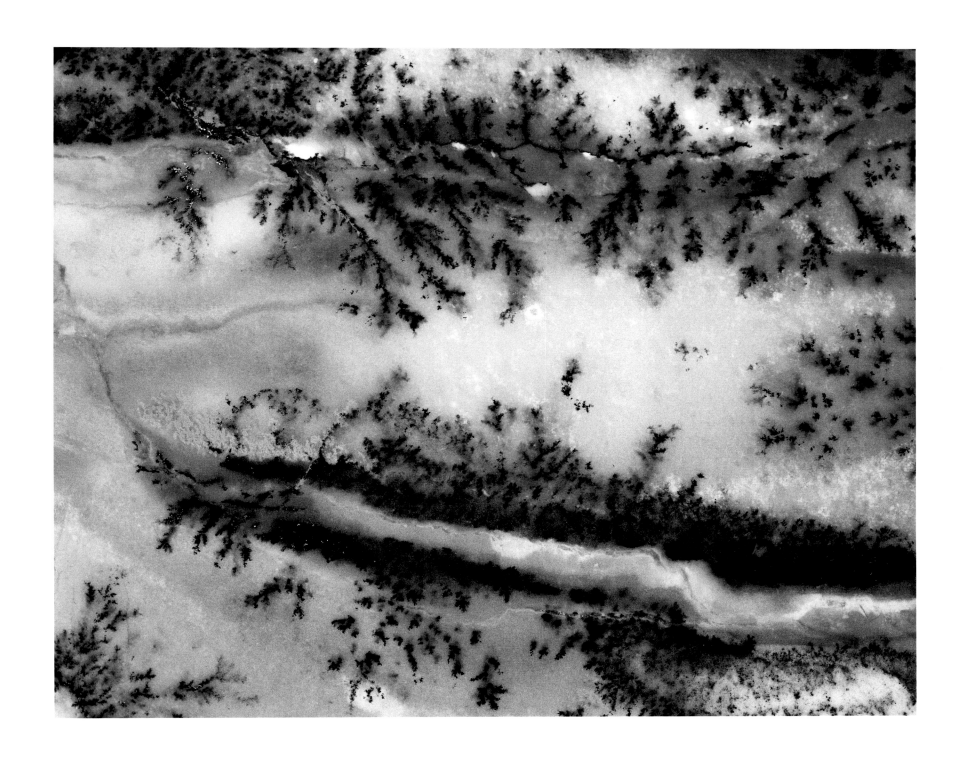

AMETHYST SAGE AGATE

Sulfur is fire. It is a destroyer.

The Byzantine Greeks dissolved it in petrol distilled from Armenian oil, and spewed it flaming from their galleys. Once lit, you couldn't douse the flames: Greek fire set the very sea alight.

The Chinese mixed it with saltpeter and charcoal, and launched missiles from bamboo cannons. Such secrets cannot stay hidden for long, and medieval Europe welcomed the explosive power of sulfur. But military surgeons cursed it, and dug deep to remove the poison that they supposed was carried by gunpowder into bullet wounds.

Mustard gas is a compound of sulfur, which first drifted in silent clouds over the muddy fields of Ypres, to burn, blister, blind and maybe to kill.

Brimstone rained down burning on Sodom and Gomorrah— a volcano, perhaps, that seemed to speak with God's voice. The next day Abraham saw smoke rising from the cities, as if from a furnace.

Sulfur is fire.

Philip Ball

MOOKAITE

This is gold from the Pactolus River, where Midas washed away the treacherous gift of Dionysus. Here I have worked it into a pair of ear-rings which depict the Great Leader in Heaven, Zeus in his Winged Chariot, just as Socrates described it. It is right to make these things from gold. I have raised the surface of the metal, see these little granules, they are balls of gold sifted from the river's sand, no bigger than a seed. Here in Thessaly we goldsmiths learn the secret of this art. You must boil the bones of a small animal or perhaps a fish, and then you must obtain some of this green stone, which we call gold glue. You grind the stone finely, and then you mix it with the glue from the bones, and it will fix the gold balls onto the fine jewellery you have crafted. Heat this in a furnace, but add to it more charcoal than you would normally, and take care that the heat is mild. Then you will find the grains of gold are united to the whole, and the metal will become lively and pleasing to the eye.

Philip Ball

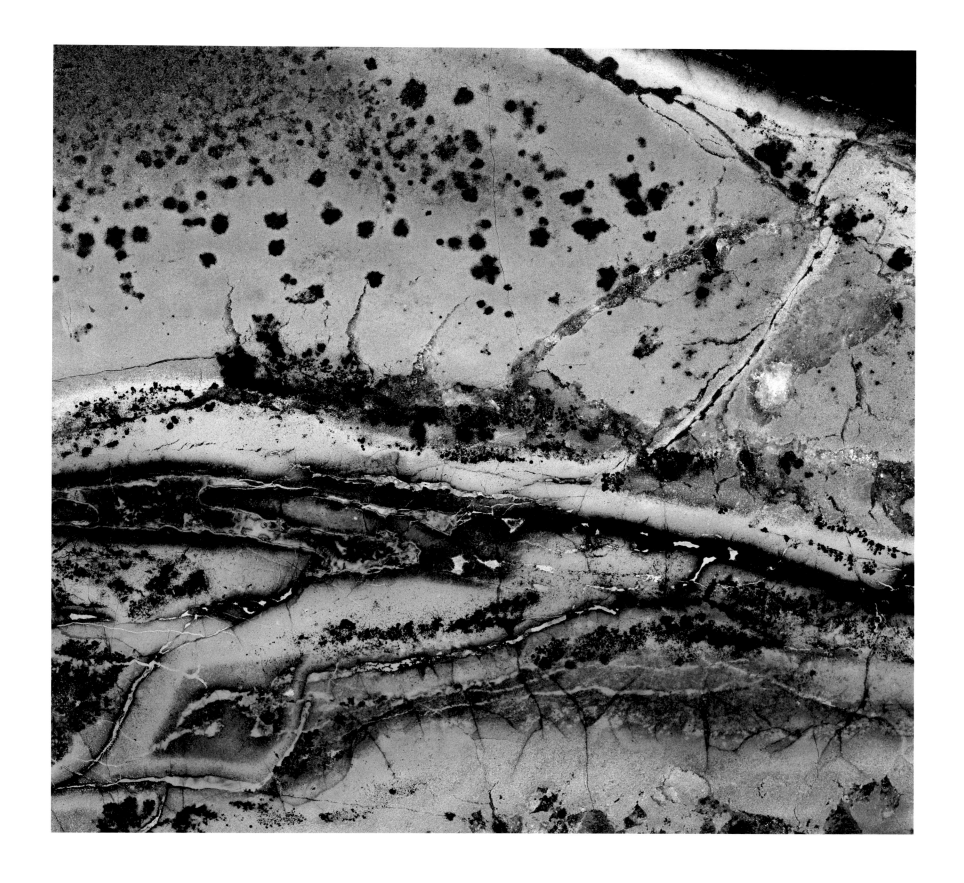

CHRYSOCOLLA

What is gold worth, when you have no iron? It is a metal that keeps
its edge—the first to possess it in quantity, the Hittites, conquered
their world. There was iron before the Iron Age, but precious little,
and the Egyptian rulers five and a half millennia ago were proud
to be seen dead with it. They called it baa-en-pet, *which is iron of*
heaven, because that was where it came from. Metal from the sky,
alloyed with nickel in the gods' crucible to save it from rust. What
a weighty gift!—scattered in sparse nuggets across the earth. One
fell in Greenland, and kept the Inuit in iron for over a century.
A hundred-pounder fell in 1492 near the German town of Ensisheim,
when the metal was no longer in short supply. But this was not
earthly stuff, it was iron of heaven and filled with the occult force of
magnetism, and the townsfolk bore it to the church, chanting psalms.
Paracelsus the Swiss alchemist came by in 1528 and pronounced it
'stone and iron'—but, like all bodies fallen from the celestial sphere,
an omen all the same.

Philip Ball

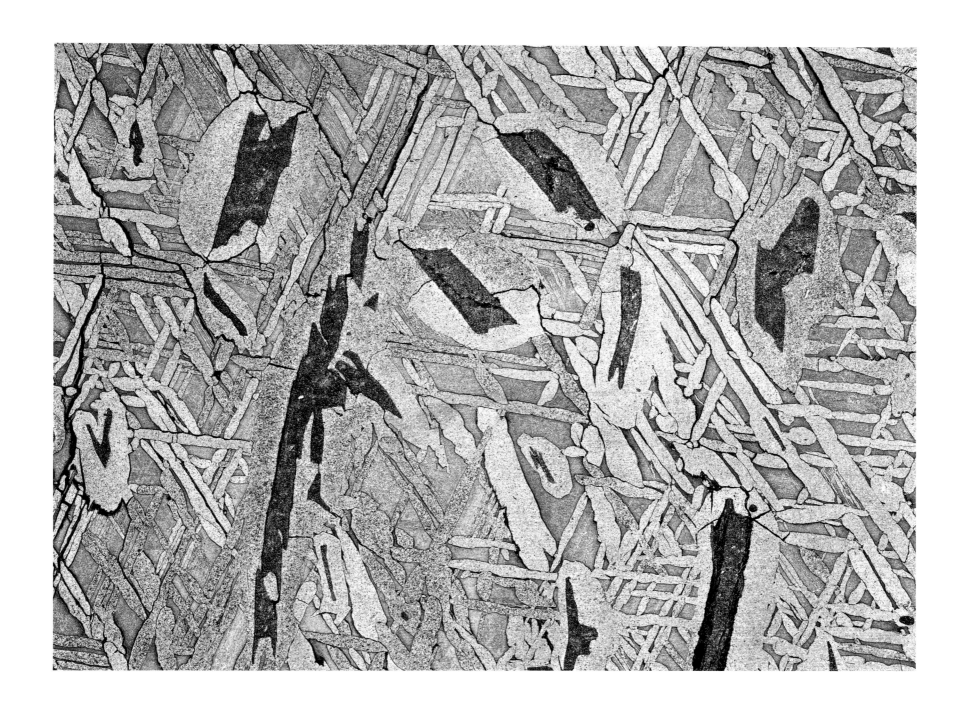

Iron Meteorite

In the magmatic glow of the furnace and forge, humans long
ago learned to extract the glint of metal from unremarkable rock.
Our soaring structures and machine-enabled potency derive mainly
from ores and the mined fuels that we have burned to extract alloys.

On occasion, people have asked themselves whether this has been a
worthwhile enterprise—particularly after steely warfare has littered
lands with corpses and shards. Some may even have been tempted to
toss our tools back into Vulcan's fires.

But we move always forward, impelled by the exultant chesty
pride that rises when "raw" materials are transformed into a plow,
a skyscraper and—yes—even a sword.

Andrew Revkin

ELEMENT

TIGER IRON

Metal Meditations

Visitors from space, like this one teach us about conditions between the orbits of Mars and Jupiter, and back to a time of crystallization that makes a chunk of petrified wood from the age of the dinosaurs seem like our close relative. When we return the visit (I am thinking about humans in orbit, but one robot craft, Voyager, has in fact passed even Pluto's orbit), we travel encased in metals, extend our own senses with metallic receivers, use wires to compute orbital routes too complex for human brains, and forge electricity as well as condition the air of spacecraft using metal-filled boxes.

Their pattern is cued to linking. Metals form long ductile networks. This ability keeps them strong against tension. We employ this potency to bridge rivers and strengthen skyscrapers. Their ductility also makes them good for conducting electricity in power and communication "pipes." By their native capability to weave webs, we connect places and each other, uniting the world and hopefully ameliorating our own tensions via metals. Metals serve humankind. But we do need to be circumspect, lest in the future the tables turn and they eat us up for evolutionary dinner and thus serve us in a different way.

Tyler Volk

ELEMENT

IRON METEORITE

Water in its three forms enables the living Earth. Its liquefied gushings and percolations liberate minerals and turn stone to soil. As ice and snow it serves as a mountaintop reservoir banked for dry times. Its vapors envelop the planet in an insulating sheath and then, embracing motes of sea salt and dust, form droplets that descend to bathe parched lands. But utility is perhaps the least of water's gifts. In all its guises—from fog to cataracts—it kidnaps photons arriving from the sun and fills our eyes with miracles.

Andrew Revkin

ELEMENT

PIETERSITE

In the higher latitudes, where Earth's tilt divides the year in seasons, autumn is life's last boisterous blaze before the cold white sleep of winter. After months of building greenness, maples flare as if consumed by fire, then shed spent leaves until the hardening ground is matted with the colors of combustion. Pigment and substance dematerialize, seeping into the soil to await the forest's resurgent physiology.

Each pole, in turn, nods toward the sun. Fed by warming rays and lengthening days, flora and fauna burst forth with an exuberance that almost seems aware of its own evanescence.

Andrew Revkin

ELEMENT

MARRA MAMBA JASPER

Science must be conservative—even while pasting us onto a membrane in a ten-dimensional universe—but that has a human cost. With his discovery of oscillating chemical reactions in the 1950s, Russian biochemist Boris Pavlovitch Belousov appeared to be violating thermodynamics: an unforgivable sin. So the work was dismissed as experimental error, and he was forced to publish his results in stealth and obscurity. Nearly 30 years later Belousov was rehabilitated and awarded the Lenin prize, but it was too late: by then he had been dead ten years. Chemical reactions, like all processes of change, are supposed to have their arrow of time oriented by thermodynamics, so the idea that they can keep switching back and forth sounded at first like heresy. But in fact oscillations are entirely possible, so long as the chemical mixture remains far from its equilibrium state. A well-stirred mixture blinks between two colors, as rhythmic as a pendulum. Leave it unstirred in a shallow tray and the oscillations spread as concentric waves and spirals. Slime molds and bacteria make these patterns, and they appear in heart tissue and in ecosystems. Oh, and in rocks too.

Philip Ball

LAW

CRAZY LACE AGATE

Origin and Radiation

Origins begin humbly, at special sites in space and time. They then radiate out, re-arranging the world into which they spread. Life, for instance, might have begun at the contact between briny water and vibrant mineral surfaces, perhaps in the deep sea's volcanic vents, hives of exotic chemical couplings. Once in full swing, bacteria changed the planet, over eons, inexorably and forever.

The air filled with oxygen, helping more complex types of cells originate and radiate. This pattern of spreading from a source shows itself in the parts of creatures, in fish fins, flower petals, octopus arms, leaves, feathers.

Our psyches, too, originate from starting points, as the earliest learned behaviors and then memories are laid down in the ripening infant brain. We grow and thereby affect the world. We reach out, to act, create, and love, to place our imprint (for the most part, gently and beautifully) on others and thus on the shared sphere of ideas. Out into every aspect of the world our psyches spread, and thereby we come to know more of the totality of repeating rhymes: from small parts to larger wholes, from infinitesimal atoms to sublime minerals, from barely visible bacteria to barely comprehensible biosphere.

Tyler Volk

SERAPHINITE

RECIPE FOR OMEGA-MINUS

You will need:

An alternating-gradient synchrotron (for making rare particles)
An 80-inch metal chamber, with a glass window of the highest optical quality
240 gallons of liquid hydrogen at close to (but not above) minus 253°C
A 31-ton magnet
A 250-pound piston
A camera and several thousand photographic plates

Enclose the chamber in the magnet, and use the piston to compress the hydrogen. Adjust the synchrotron to produce K-mesons, and direct the mesons into the chamber. Collisions with the hydrogen's protons will create omega-minus particles. Release the piston by half an inch within 0.015 seconds, dropping the pressure. This brings the hydrogen to the brink of boiling, so that heat released by the passage of omega-minus particles vaporizes it to make a string of bubbles, curled by the magnetic field. Photograph these at a fast speed. You may need to repeat thousands of times to get the bubble track you want.

This recipe was first devised at Brookhaven National Laboratory in 1964. The bubbles of the omega-minus revealed the symmetry of the subatomic world, allowing all heavy particles to be classified in a scheme called the Eightfold Way which brought order to this Lilliputian menagerie.

Philip Ball

LAW

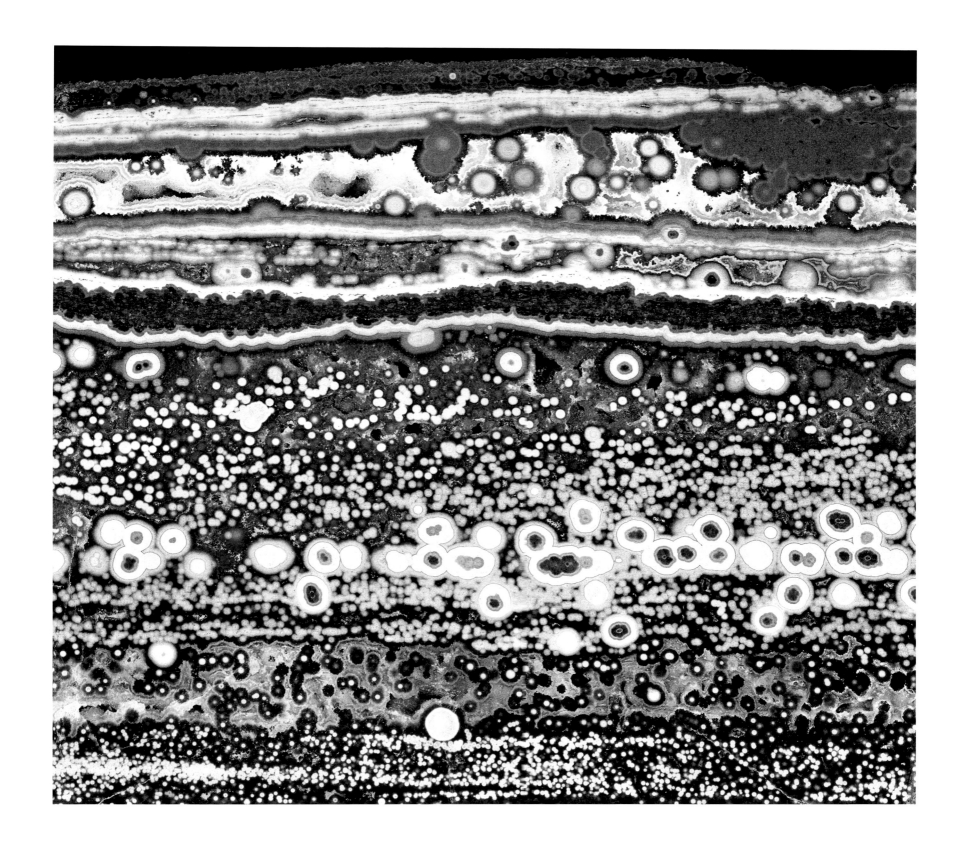

OCEAN JASPER

COOL CRYSTALLIZATIONS

*A clock's second is proportional to a human century as a single year
is to the immensity of one hundred and forty million centuries.
It's this cosmic stretch we must imagine to go all the way back
to the birth of our universe. After the instantaneous bursting
forth of existence at the Big Bang, the expanding infant universe
quickly cooled. As it did it underwent a series of fractionations—
snap, crackle, pop. Fundamental forces, from the strong nuclear force
to the grip of gravity, each separated out in turn. The universe kept
cooling. Protons and neutrons condensed and then formed nuclei
from a hot viscous sea of energized quarks. Expanding more, it cooled
further. The simplest atoms of hydrogen and helium froze out when
electrons, in turn, crystallized from the sea into partnerships with the
nuclei. Gravity churned at the big scales, gathering matter into giant
galaxies, stars, and solid bodies, such as our compact, spinning Earth.*

*Today, magma upchucked from Earth's geological guts carries on the
tale of fractionation. When cooled, atoms in the magma crystallize
into visible networks of minerals. There's more: Human ideas also
crystallize. One way to ease the creation of concepts happens during
cool times of concentration, of focused chilling out, during calm
meditation. Isn't that when you can often discern what it is that is
most vital to think about? Isn't that when the freshest ideas, from our
subconscious sea, often come forth and take on conscious shape?*

Tyler Volk

LAW

GRAPHIC GRANITE

Concentricity is commonplace in nature—in tree rings and bone and coral and stone, in the rings of Saturn, in the structure of the atmosphere. Layer upon layer forms, sometimes in sequence and sometimes forged en masse as constituents in a primordial brew segregate and settle according to laws of density or repulsion and attraction.

It is also a characteristic of humanity, both the individual and society. Sturdy layers accrete around the soul, guarding against unwelcome truths. Walls, locks, fences, and armies provide an impermeable perimeter against communal fears.

But there is a cost in concentricity. While closed circles allow no intrusion, they also stifle contact, comprehension, and communion.

Andrew Revkin

LAW

MALACHITE

Reaching Oneness

*Within the variegated, multi-scaled, often seemingly arbitrary, and
even confounding mess of the intricate world resides utter simplicity.
This simplicity can be a shape, such as the sphere: Florence's Duomo
and Rome's Pantheon, a soccer ball, the egg case of a spider, a ripe
grape on the vine. Physics got there even before architecture, sports,
or biology. Foam laps up onto beaches as bubbles. Droplets of dew
on leaves make water defy gravity. In compact units inside rocks,
minerals in special sites reflect the tendency for like to clump with like,
both inwards and outwards, giving shape to omnidirectional patterns
that resemble that of the giant Earth and the nearly circular orbits of
our planets.*

*The inner simplicity is also apparent from another angle. It's
the oneness bestowed by principles that unify. For instance, the
properties of the mathematical sphere hold true for any specific
sphere: this singular shape has a minimized surface and maximized
volume. Such inner principles become revealed not by breaking
in with a hammer blow but by subtle probing with insight, more
powerful than any physical tool because of its potential scope. What
kinds of oneness remain to be found? What kinds of oneness are
beneath the fundamental constants of physics, within the biodiversity
and stability of ecosystems, inside human beliefs, anxieties, and joys?*

Tyler Volk

LAW

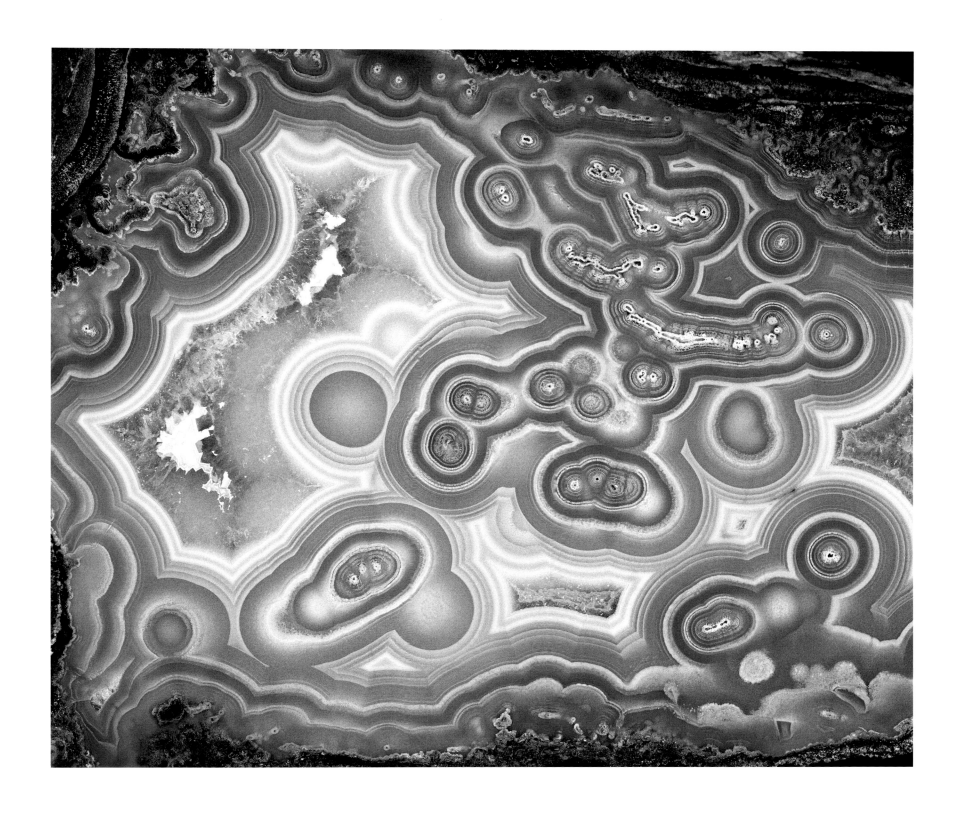

AGUA NUEVA AGATE

This looks to me like one of those times, deep in the future, when
turquoise-colored nanotubes, growing on their own, the blue alveoli
of intelligent lungs, wrap their tendrils around the atmosphere
of a formerly poisonous planet. There are other interpretations.
I guess I was about eight when I was most entranced with my hobby
collecting minerals. My stepfather was a crystallographer, and his
parents, jewelers in Mount Vernon, gave me a little bound sampler
containing chips of semi-precious stones: beryl, chrysotile, jasper, rose
quartz, calcite, and so on. Encouraging my interest he took me to
a mineral show. There was a raffle with door prizes and everyone
received a newspaper with a hefty mineral egg—an agate, drab on
the outside, spectacular within. We all had use of rock hammers
but we were encouraged, before the purple revelation, to trade our
enigmatic agates as much as we liked. Unable to resist temptation,
I switched mine at least once. I kept track of the one I traded away,
which ended up in the hands of a twelve-year-old boy. I was
disappointed. I should have kept the original. Rock on.

Dorion Sagan

LAW

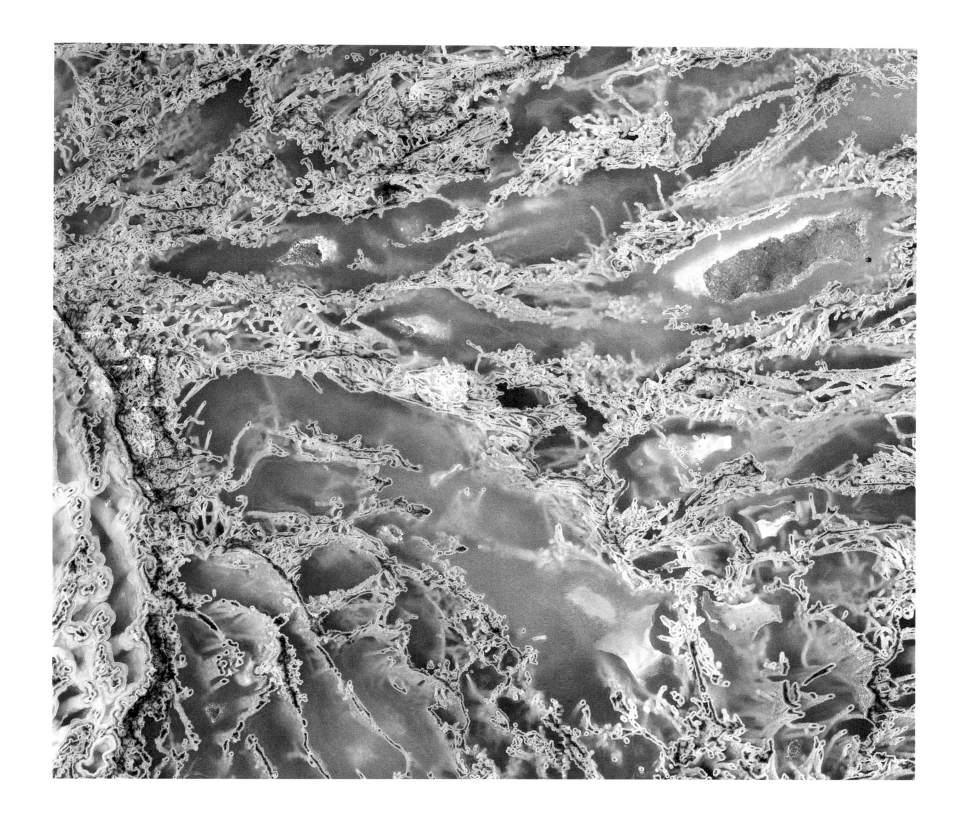

MOSS AGATE

SECLUSION AND WISDOM

*Protection succors inner growth, as shell of nut helps seed, as womb
serves fetus, as skull sustains brain. Consider the colorful crystal
delights that develop within a protective ball of mineralized mud.
To enlarge, they feed on the fluids that seep through. Thus when
seclusion is truly dynamic and creative it is linked to movement.
The fetus emerges, the seed sprouts, the brain plays.*

*Our innermost self can deepen in wisdom, even as the aging body
hardens and skin becomes less supple and bones more brittle, and
as seclusion is cherished to a greater extent. To nourish this growth,
we can draw anytime upon a plentiful supply of fluids from the
world. (Just think of what is available!) Both protect and bathe the
innermost being. It can stay growing all the way until death. Along
that wondrous path, friends and loved ones rejoice in what emanates
from your refined forms. You may take pleasure in the delights of
your own inner world as well, directly, by reaping what arises within
the cracks of introspection.*

Tyler Volk

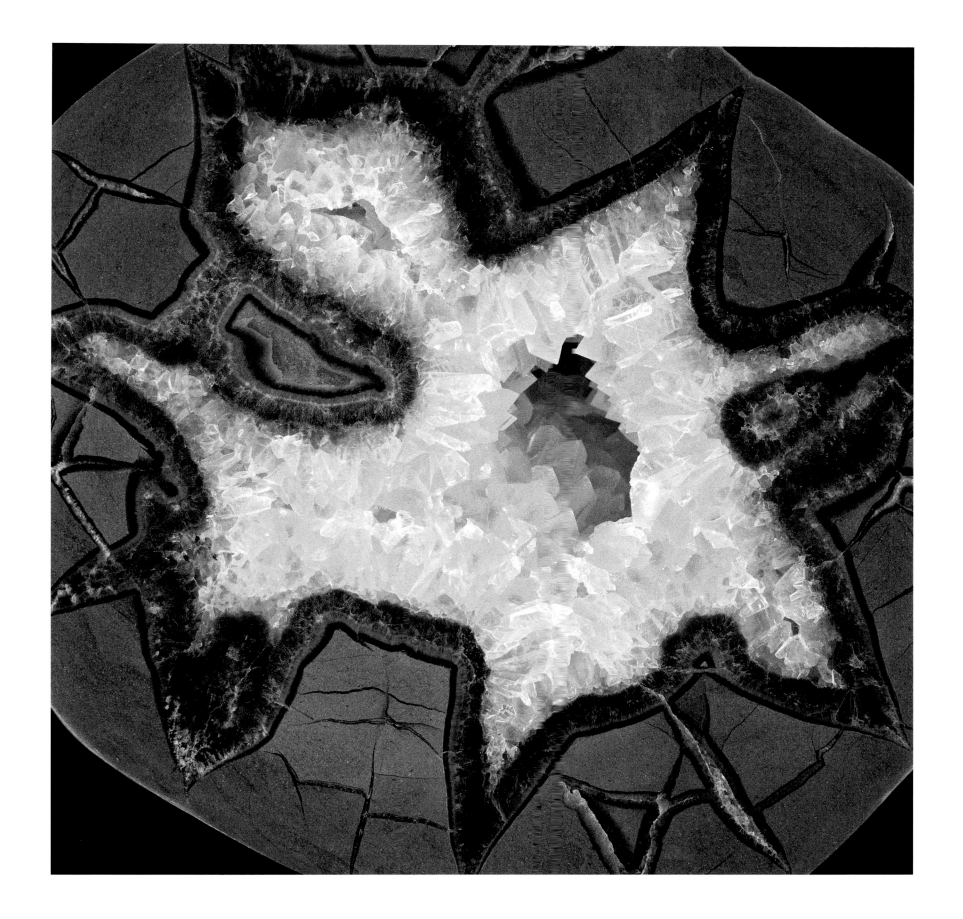

SEPTARIUM

An exponent of the grattage *technique developed by Max Ernst, Romy Dechlau combined it with the methods of the Old Masters to achieve a pictorial surface with depth and dynamism. 'There is no point trying to escape the past,' he said, 'because you won't succeed.' The revelation—one might say the invention—of hidden form is what Leonardo had in mind when he said of random patches on a wall that 'if you look at them carefully enough, you will make some wonderful discoveries.' In Ernst's* grattage *(scraping) there is a genuine dis-covering, as layers of paint are scratched away to reveal others beneath. For Dechlau's* Sixth Seal, *shown here, patches of color were applied to the canvas and then pulled across it while still wet with a straight-edged implement. 'The pressure I exert and the direction my hand takes', he explained, 'are determined in the moment by the shape I see unfolding.' The textures are clearly apocalyptic—rising flames, splashes of brimstone, streaking comets—as befits the 'great earthquake' and the stars that 'fell to earth' when the sixth seal is broken. Meanwhile, Dechlau's colors and forms refer us to John Martin's* Destruction of Sodom and Gomorrah *(1852).*

Philip Ball

ART

PIETERSITE

There is a cave, dimly lit and mostly shadows. Within this prison of rock, a lost people live out their lives; they believe the cave is the whole of the world. One day, in a heap of rubble, the shaman finds a stone. It is of opal, and from its depths blazes a living fire. Within this single stone shine suns and stars, crescent moons and white-ringed planets, clouds of glowing gas and galaxies—even entire universes. The shaman sees all this. He beats his drum and dances in joy and howls out in exaltation at the immense glory of life. He begins showing his magic stone to others of his tribe. But the chieftain, jealous and wroth, grabs up the stone and smashes it to pieces, and then uses rocks to grind it into dust. He orders the shaman's tongue cut out with sharp flints that he should never tell anyone of impossible wonders. The chieftain contents himself that he has kept his people from dreaming dangerous dreams that would upset the peace of the tribe.

But then one day, the shaman gathers up the opal dust and mixes it with oil. He goes into the deepest, darkest part of the cave where no one ever goes. And he paints. And on the smooth, cracked walls of the cave he brings forth suns and stars, crescent moons and white-ringed planets, clouds of glowing gas and galaxies—even entire universes. And so, at last, he escapes the cave. Many years later he dies knowing that anyone who is willing to look for gems in rubble and light within the dark will escape, too —

David Zindell

ART

FLUORITE-OPAL NODULE

Dreaming of Early Consciousness

*We are in a university lab. We are dreaming. Cooperative white
lab rats are trained to seek and locate a food treat at an object, say
a small cylinder, which is shifted at each trial. The rats are also
able to find food according to space, established by a rat room with
dissimilar walls. But they have limits. They fail when the goal lies
between a certain wall and a constantly shifted cylinder. Human
infants also fail. But toddlers can make the leap. Toddlers, like adults,
use images in complex combinations, in higher levels of patterning.
An enhanced ability "to combine" seems to be a primary difference
between animals and us. Some psychologists have evidence that this
ability is related to language. Language enriches our images, our
pictures, our dreams.*

*We are in an ancestral cave in Australia. We are dreaming. In
our paintings, colorful polka dots float and form larger patterns
of roundels and paths, overall portraits of "dreamings." These
multi-layered mappings of landscape, mythology, and thought allure
us because they guide us inward to what we all share, to the place
where language and image both merge and mutually reinforce, to
where, perhaps, we find the roots of cognitive capabilities that evolved
at the dawn of human consciousness.*

Tyler Volk

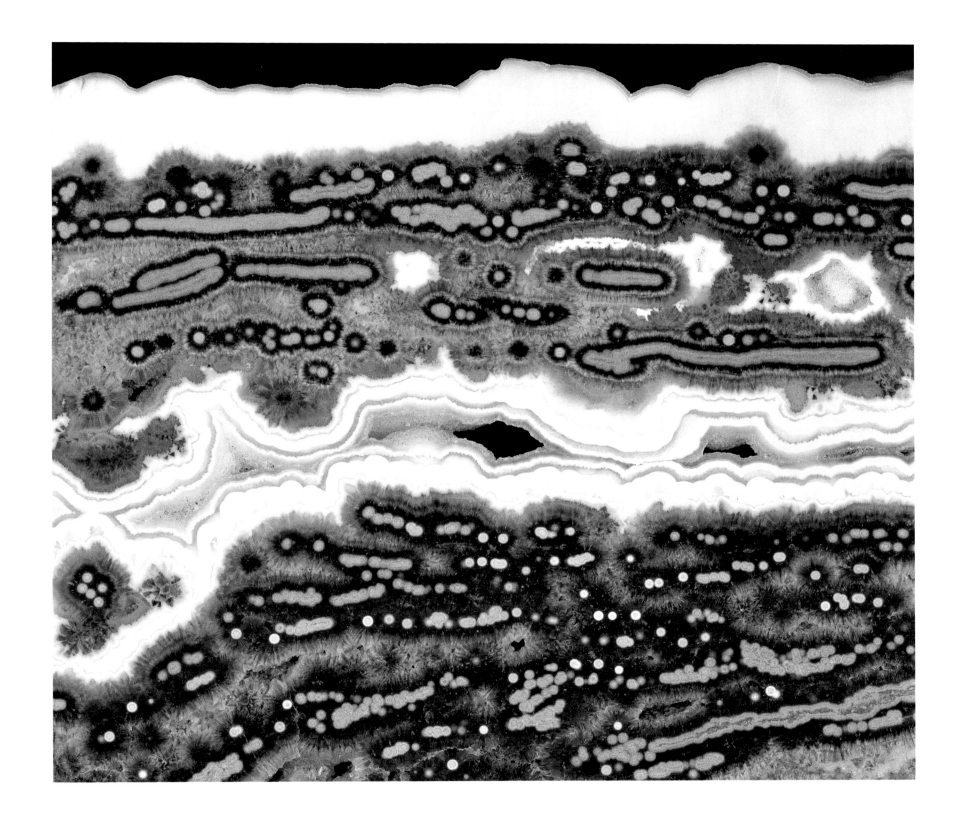

OCEAN JASPER

CURIOUS PATHS

*Thirty thousand years ago, with the benefits and insights from new
layers of consciousness, humans in bands trekked the valleys of ice
age Europe. They filled these valleys with trails, encampments, cave
dwellings, sites for crafting tools. Songs rang out and helped tame
the wild spaces. The ancients followed migrating herds, moving
between summer and winter sites, gathering into larger bands for
celebrations and mating opportunities. They employed the primal
color, perhaps the first color to be civilized—red ochre—taken from
minerals and used on cave walls, on faces during dances and war,
on corpses prepared for burial with necklaces of carnivore teeth.
In their imaginations, the valleys changed from true wilderness to
zones filled by the mind, with memories, fears, dreams, adventures,
pain, conquests, loves, myths. The world was no longer just sensed
but layered with projected cultural patterns. Cliffs and clouds took on
faces. Streams talked.*

*Curiosity fills our genes. Some explorer is always ready for wider
adventure. Thus new paths are shaped, new lands and concepts
sought. There is always the tension: to stay comfortable or break out.
Ultimately, how do we balance this tension? One way to go from
known to unknown is by oozing outwards.*

Tyler Volk

ART

Owyhee Picture Jasper

Perhaps we tamed fire. Perhaps fire tamed us. Certainly we are still seduced by that glowing dance of a thousand roseate veils, whether in the shimmering heat of the hearth or the growl of the V-8.

While water soothes and nourishes, fire empowers. The astonishing magic of controlled combustion, facilitated by Earth's just-right atmosphere and ample stores of fuels, has allowed humans to transform from scattered gatherers into a gathering global force.

Fire transports us, and in return we transport fire. Together, for better and worse, we have made the world our own.

Andrew Revkin

MUNJINA STONE

Où, teignant tout à coup les bleuités, délires

Et rhythmes lents sous les rutilements du jour,

Plus fortes que l'alcool, plus vastes que nos lyres,

Fermentent les rousseurs amères de l'amour!

J'ai rêvé la nuit verte aux neiges éblouies,

Baiser montant aux yeux des mers avec lenteurs,

La circulation des sèves inouïes,

Et l'éveil jaune et bleu des phosphores chanteurs!

Arthur Rimbaud (Le Bateau ivre)

Where, suddenly staining the bluenesses, deliriums,

And dull rhythms with a sunburst of russet needles,

The bitter rednesses of love ferment,

Stronger than alcohol, more piercing than our lyres.

I have dreamed the green night of dazzled frazil,

Kiss rising slowly to the eyes of the seas,

The circulation of seminal saps,

The yellow and blue arousal of the phosphorescent singers.

Arthur Rimbaud (The Drunken Boat)
trans. Robert Hutchinson

PIETERSITE

There is no blue so profoundly healing as the hue

radiating from each bulging swell of the farthest reaches

of the Pacific Ocean. Memories of that color are a refuge

for me and prompted a song once, which echoed as I first

swam in this image.

When my life is over, Lord, don't take me in the sky.

The blue above it pales beside the blue Pacific wide.

Let me take my final rest out on the velvet sea.

Let the water take the weight of life's burdens from me.

Blue, blue, Pacific blue, ease my tired soul.

Blue, blue, Pacific blue, bathe me in your glow.

Blue, blue, Pacific blue, carry me away.

Blue, blue, Pacific blue, the color never fades.

Andrew Revkin

BLACK OPAL

Purple stands for blood, as Homer said. He called it porphyra, *which became the* purpura *of the Romans. The purple of emperors, according to Pliny, was the color of clotted blood. After all, millions died in its making; but they were shellfish. Each creature yields a single drop of the dye, and it is clear until sunlight turns it sanguine. Their graveyards still litter the Mediterranean coast: piles of shells shattered by the Phoenicians, who learned how to extract the dye from their god Melkarth. Dyeing was a smelly business; some say that is why the Phoenicians were ejected from Crete. Maybe their very name carries their colour: from* phoinos, *blood-red. Their art was always costly, and jealously guarded. Under Valentinian II, Romans paid with their own blood for illegal manufacture of the purple of Tyre.*

Then the West forgot how to make Tyrian purple for four hundred years. But when it was rediscovered in 1856, no one cared—for that was the year of William Perkin's mauve, the first synthetic aniline dye. At first, Perkin tried to sell it under the trade name Tyrian purple.

For Homer, the sea was purple, as though that too were drenched in blood.

Philip Ball

RHODONITE

Waiting for the Chariot

Pulling back the drapes, she watched the lilac hour swarm across the sky, complete with color express rumbling on the horizon trailing puffs of red smoke, and pastel tongues that ululated every note of lavender. Imparadised, eyes chanting color, color, color, she craned her neck to see past the edge of the window frame for the first sign of the satellite which . . . she checked her watch . . . in six minutes would begin its transit from west to east across the evening sky. What deep indigo skirts the heavens were twirling. But soon a tiny cymbal would appear against the darkness at one edge of her vision, a piece of glitter skating briskly toward the east. As the seconds drew closer, she leaned against the back of the sofa and relaxed. There was no need to strain. It would soon be there, a beautiful sequin filling the dusk, if only for a moment, with its small stabbing light.

Diane Ackerman

CHAROITE

SYNESTHESIA

In Desert Solitaire, *nature-loving curmudgeon Edward Abbey*
demands that we see mesas, cacti, clouds not as signs denoting
something else but solely as themselves. This is mystical vision,
in which our cognitive filters fall away and things shine in their
naked glory. Supposedly. But our brains persist in thwarting pure
perception. Our neural circuits are so tightly packed and interwoven
that even the simplest percepts reverberate throughout our lobes,
evoking memories, metaphors, analogies—whether or not we want
them. Synesthesia is a particularly literal outcome of short-circuiting
between sensory pathways: you see the opalescence of your lover's
sigh, hear her scent as a distant flute, feel her gaze feather your belly.
Bereft of neural crosstalk, we would also lack language, art, music,
mathematics—all our modes of making meaning and sense, and
of imagining. We would be trapped in the point-like prison of the
here and now. Shouldn't we celebrate—rather than suppressing—
the innate flightiness that propels our minds back and forth through
space and time? And isn't seeing one thing in another—thou art that,
and so on—a mystic trait too?

John Horgan

MIND

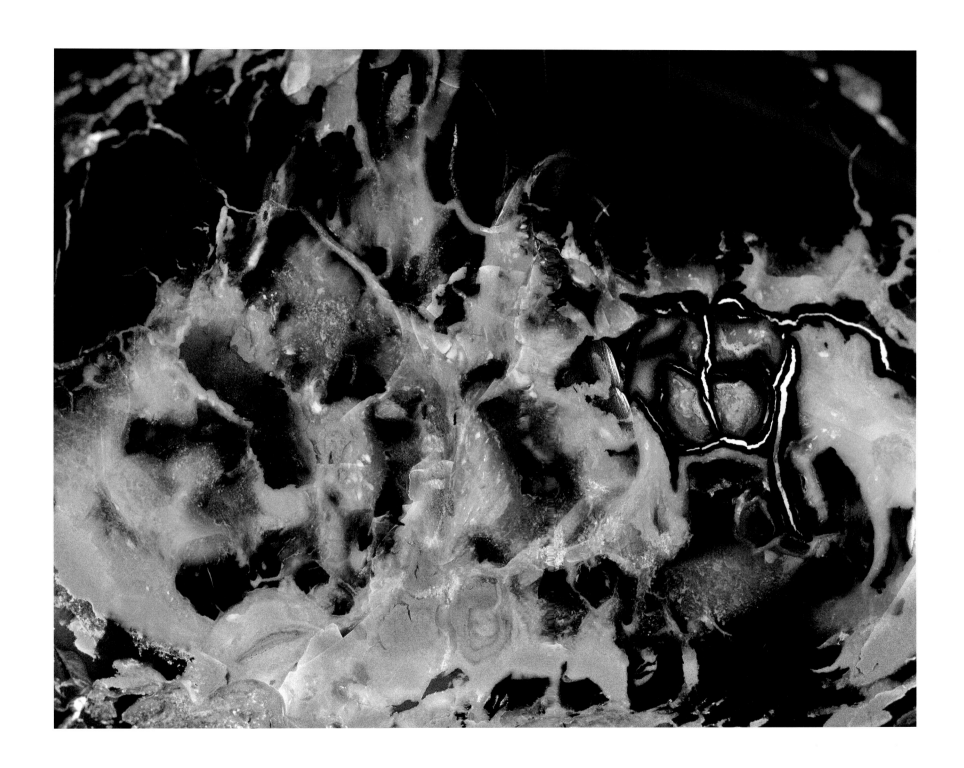

MATRIX OPAL

*By mistake I once ate too much marijuana and was gifted with the
most fantastic experience. Stoned out of my mind (or perhaps, in a
certain way, more truly in my mind than I had ever been before)
I put on some great music and lay back to listen to it. And I saw
the music. The technical term for this is synesthesia, the mixing up
of the senses, and this sounds terrifying. But I found it beautiful.
The photo of this rock brings to mind the photo of this experience
that burns—or sings—in my memory.*

*Look at the central, broken black line as it rises and falls from left to
right, like a sine wave; it's like looking into the very heart of sound.
Striations of gold, green and red, generated by the wave and glowing
as with a light within, are the very colors of the melody: the tones
of trumpets, oboes, and vibrating strings. Above and below the
wave gleam complex and richly textured patterns of bronze and
ocher, black, white, and a redder red. These are the larger patterns
crystalized out of the music—call them phrases, sustained chords,
or melodic ornamentation. The whole of it adds up to a symphony
of shimmering sound and makes me wonder: why should rocks sing?*

David Zindell

MIND

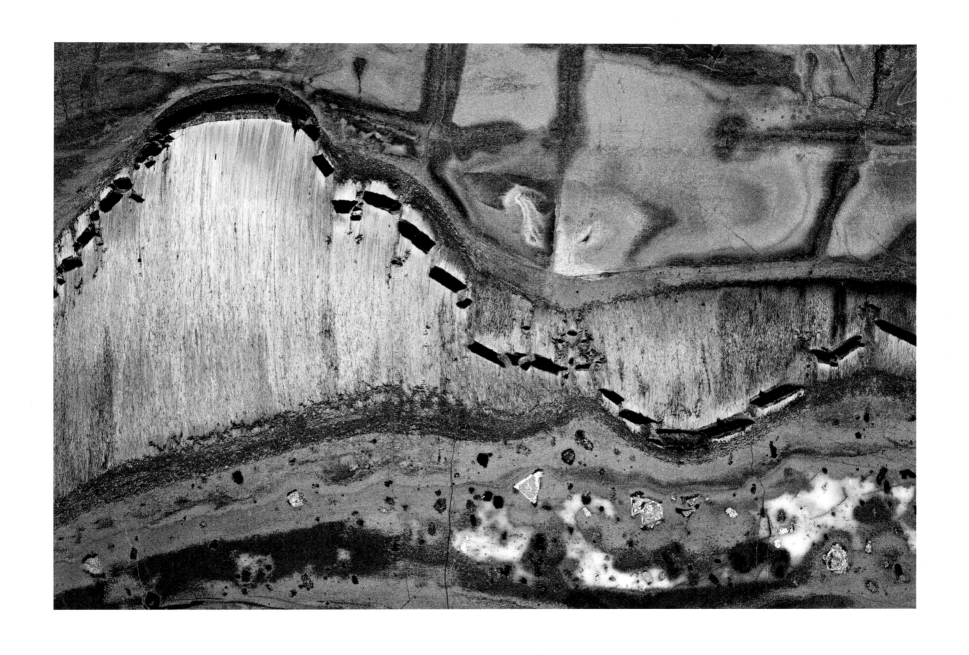

MARRA MAMBA TIGER'S-EYE

Liquid music, a balletscape of ice skaters trapped in one of Chekov's
unwritten stories, murmuring in the language of light how some day
they will escape through the mist, and visit us in the future. There
their dance of light, the hard rock café where they build a moon rocket,
inhaling the smell of ballerinas, and promising in the mist. Ovid tells
us of all those who were turned into trees, and here I do think we see
her, the ballerina who was trapped, preserved forever as virgin in
the pristine morning of a new day, the pure hope of tomorrow caught
in ice. One day we will know what she thinks, see the blue crescent
which is not the moon.

Dorion Sagan

MIND

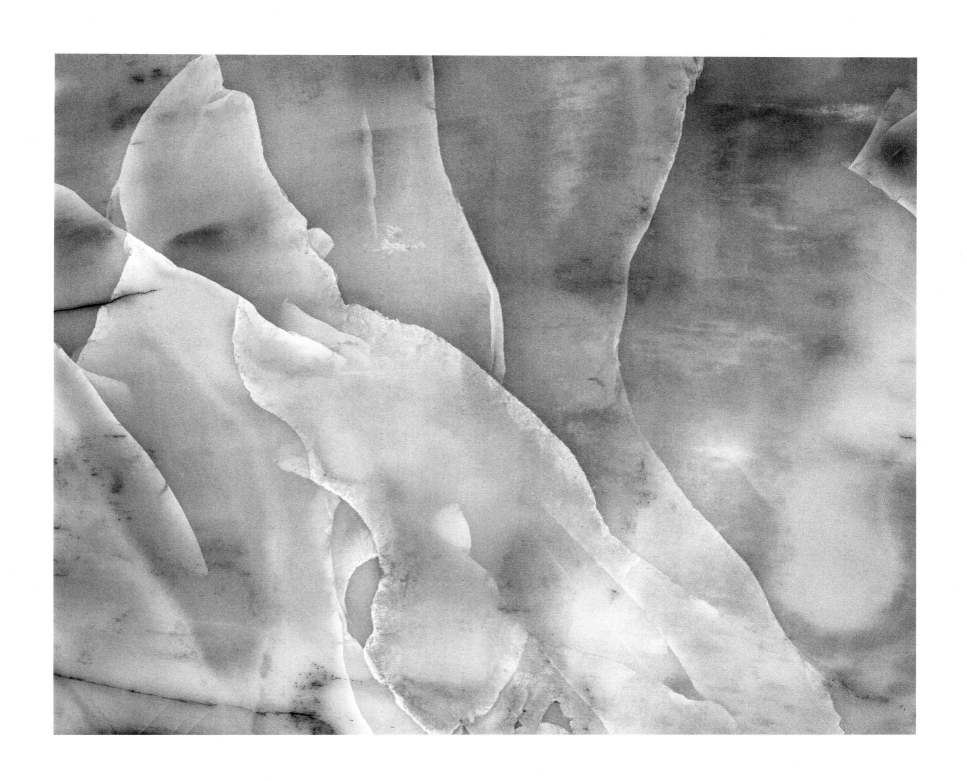

PETRIFIED WOOD

A Lapidarian's Checklist

the step stones of flirtation,
and the eyes frisky as moonstone,
and the whetstone of wit,
and the loose pebbles of laughter,
and the shale of uncertainty,
and the quicksand of infatuation,
and the gold foil of kisses,
and the bakestone of passion,
and the magnetite of nuzzling,
and the rare-earth of deep play,
and the wavy strata of memories,
and the bedrock of powwows,
and the paydirt of rapture,
and the milestones of courtship,
and the alabaster of shared dreams
and the rippling agate of linked fates,
and the old chalk of monotony,
and the pumice of cold shoulders,
and the pillow lava of neglect,
and the grindstone of blame,
and the landslide of putdowns,
and the bluffs of loneliness
and the palisades of low spirit,
and the fool's gold of witty rant
and the sandblast of self-esteem,
and the gravestone of desire,
and the rock-ribbed you always,
and the mossy boulder of rejection,
and the branching coral of hope,
and the opal geyser of hilarity
and the crystal of come-hithers,
and the side-glances of flowing mercury

Diane Ackerman

MIND

Banded Agate

Psychedelic Night Terrors

The only hallucinogen known to occur naturally in the human brain—as well as in diverse plants, fungi, and other animals— is dimethyltryptamine. DMT's chemical structure resembles that of both serotonin, the ubiquitous neurotransmitter, and lysergic acid diethylamide, whose peculiar psychotropic properties were discovered in 1943 by the Swiss chemist Albert Hofmann. DMT is the primary active ingredient of cohoba *and* ayahuasca, *plant-based preparations ingested as sacraments by South American Indians. Pure DMT is not orally active, but in the mid-1950s Stephen Szara, a Hungarian pharmacologist, found that DMT injected intravenously delivers the equivalent of a 10-hour LSD trip compressed into less than an hour. Subjects often return convinced that they have glimpsed a real heaven or hell, populated with real angels or demons. When doses exceed a certain threshold, you emerge from the experience panic-stricken but remembering nothing, like children who awake screaming from night terrors. At these doses, perhaps, DMT transports you too deeply into the* mysterium tremendum, *where you bump up against what the philosopher Alan Watts called "the taboo against knowing who you really are." One wonders: What if we possessed neurotechnical tools—microelectrode arrays, superfast magnetic-resonance imaging, high-definition electroencephalography—that would allow us to extract these buried DMT visions from subjects' brains? What sublime nightmare would we see?*

John Horgan

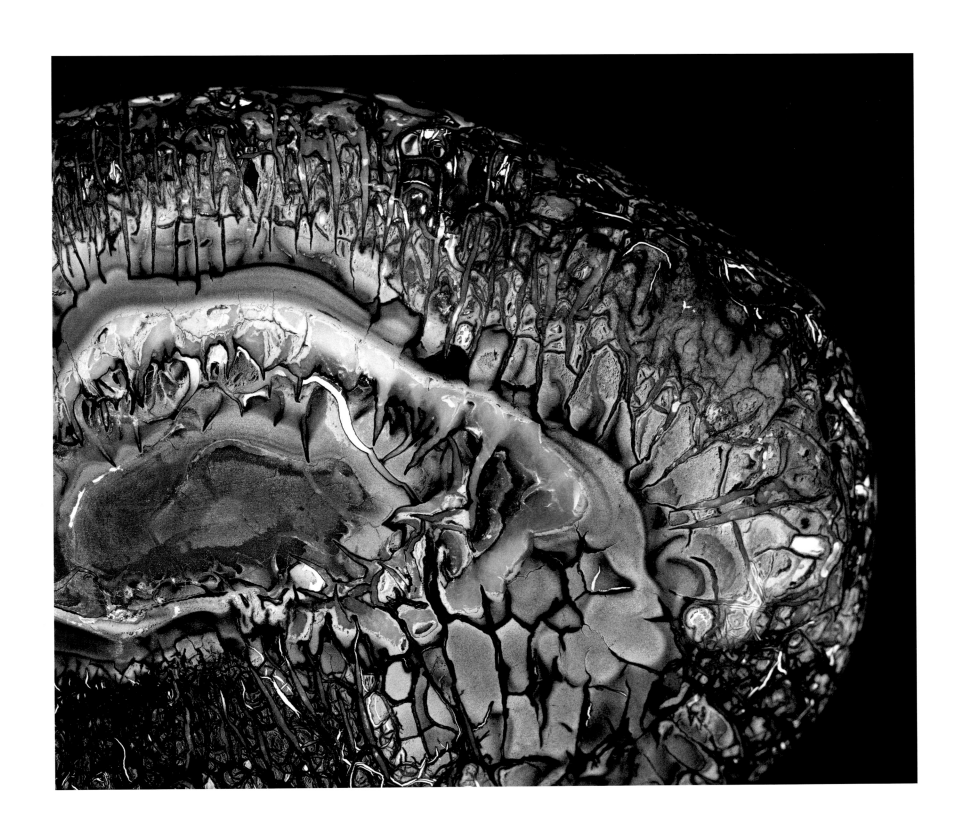

KOROIT NUT OPAL

Cold, frightening, almost machinelike. Merciless intelligence.
Terence McKenna told of mushroom-touched hallucinations that
looked so nothing like this. Triangles, quadrilaterals, almost-parallel
lines that go nowhere—nightmare geometry. A mad logic that I can
never quite grasp. Petrified neurons, fractures, a spider's leg, blood.
Utterly repellent: if a room's walls were lined with this, I'd go running
screaming out of it. And yet it is weirdly and compellingly beautiful,
too. If someone gave me a chunk of it, I'd carry it in my pocket and
bring it out to marvel at when I dared.

David Zindell

MIND

PAESINA MARBLE

Sands for a Desert Ouija Board

Though I may only taste you here
where fingers caress keys, and mind
shimmies to you sitting sandy and naked
among naked rocks, may only hold you
between mood and machine in a russet
and umber sense-luscious mind-glow,
I can feel your skin glide down my breasts
your soft quagmire slide between ribs
and hollows, where time halts in folds,
folds in upon itself and spirit flies
over bony mountains and dives below
the voice of streams, carrying me
to another you whose name I never knew
in rage, and married more than once to save.

Diane Ackerman

BODY

MOOKAITE

This stone is a painting of a poem—or is it a poem of a painting?
Or just a beautiful poem? On the upper left, male and female, yang
and yin, white and black, sperm and egg. Each is surrounded by coils
of mystic life energy. They meet, in love. There is an explosion into
infinite possibilities. Then crystallization and articulation, more and
deeper life, a sense of the shimmering layers of being that life unfolds.
And all this occurs here on earth beneath a red, rising sun.

It is a poem of rhythm and rhyme, as the regularity and conformity of
the red, rose and white bands flowing outward suggest. The repetition
of the spikes of the bands suggests a poem of much alliteration; their
valleys ring with assonance. And the bands themselves? Layers of
skin or of the petals of a rose. So I think this is a love poem, an ode to
a beautiful woman, an appreciation of her skin, as glorious as a rose,
and the even greater glories that lie within.

David Zindell

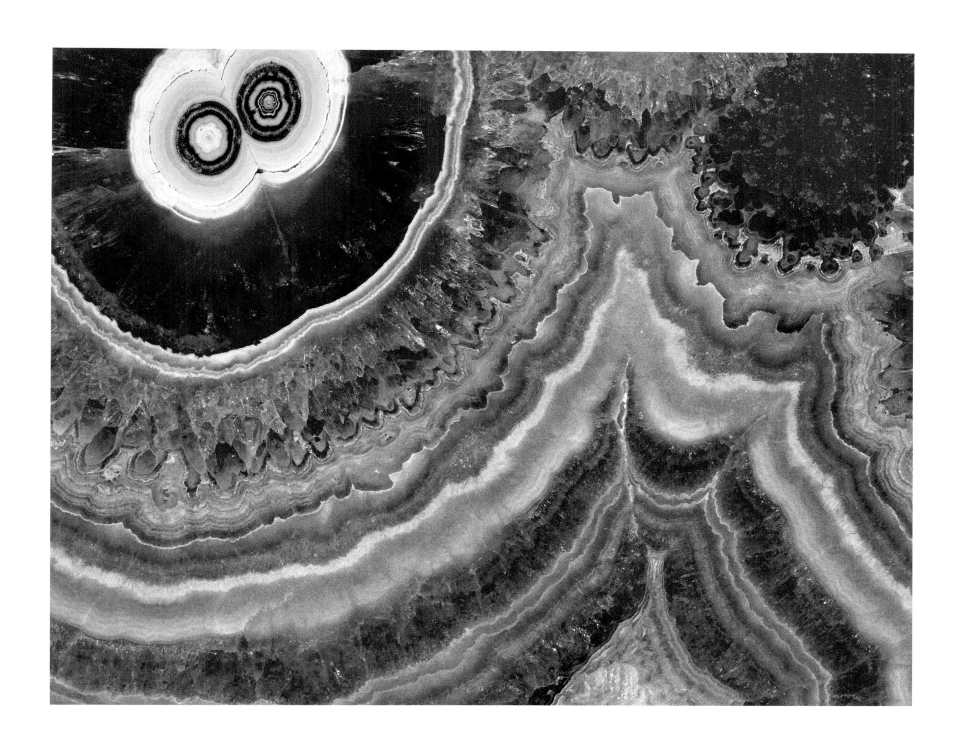

RHODOCHROSITE

This would taste like any other sodium nitrite steeped sound wave travelling vaginally at the speed of rock. You can see where she pierced herself in red candy waves, the peppermint arch of the stiletto. Although there is clearly a heart here, seen sideways and in the process of breaking, the rent has been rendered permanent, the crack of an agate whip, the stylus penetrating like a petrified lava lamp in search of a subterranean smile.

Dorion Sagan

BODY

HICKORYITE

Erotica Geologica

You are an arctic drumlin
with tundra skin,
cool atop your permafrost,
thinking yourself impregnable to all
but snow and caribou hooves.

You cannot feel me, yet,
below you, a magma pool percolating,
thrusting through fissures
fiery blades that crystallize
into dikes of gabbro, sills
of andesite, pockets
of steaming hornblende phenocrysts,
stoping the strata that roof my chamber,
fossil-laden slabs sinking
back through molten time.

And there is time
in this igneous gloom:
an epoch to envision the smoothness
of your aphanitic plutons;
an era to foresee each fold and furrow
of your alluvial fan.
Mankind will crumble to caliche
before I know the thousand faces
of your olivine eyes.

John Horgan

BODY

MORRISONITE

PETRIFIED

Oh the sadness of a tree, its to and phloem gone,
once bristling with leaf and squirrelly limbs
favored by tart sparrows and 80-year-old owls,
roots a bustling lab of phantom green,
and canopy a big blowy umbrella,

reduced to this: a rock that in the hand
feels smooth as muscle, shiny as oiled thigh,
roundly inviting as prayer beads,
touchable here like breast, there like buttocks,
a voluptuous harp of twanging flesh,

but spineless, barkless, stone cold dead.

Diane Ackerman

PETRIFIED WOOD

Once, beloved, you were alive. You were rings of cellulose singing
with sap, quivering with purpose, delighting in being but unaware
of your own delight. The tree of which you were a part stood alone
on winter nights shimmering in the moonlight. What was your color?
Ivory? Cherry? Ebony? Encased in bark, with no living eye to behold
you, what sense even to say you had a color? Did you even care?

You lived almost forever, but then you died. You lived long, long ago,
so there were no chainsaws or pulp mills for you. Neither were you
made into a frame to bring a little life to dead, pretentious paintings.
You didn't rot. Time preserved you. Time transformed you, a bit
of silica replacing fiber, trickles of hematite and cobalt dissolving
your cells and preserving them so vividly and indestructibly.
A time came when you glowed with colors: russets and teals,
flecks of black embedded in white, roses and greens and golds.
You were a glory of the earth but you remained yet unaware.

Now, beloved, you are still alive. Your heart is stone, but what
marvelous stone! My heart beats more delightedly to behold you.
My eye has framed you. In a different way—neither lesser nor
greater—you live again and forever.

David Zindell

BODY

Petrified Wood

The Petrified Mother

*In 1999, on a drizzly afternoon in Basel, Switzerland, I found
myself wandering through an exhibition called Anatomy Art,
which consisted of scores of human corpses that a German anatomist,
Gunther von Hagens, had preserved in epoxy and posed in whimsical
ways. The "Chessplayer" hunched over a board, his body flayed to
highlight the information-processing network formed by his eyeballs,
brain, and spinal column. The skinless "Runner" was captured in
full stride, scarlet muscles peeling away from his limbs like streamers.
"Reclining Mother" sprawled on her side, bathing-beauty fashion,
a window cut into her swollen belly to reveal the eight-month-old
fetus curled within. Von Hagens had skinned her skull but left intact
her nose, lips, eyes, and eyelids, fringed with lush lashes. Terrible,
that final touch of femininity. And yet once the reflexive horror
subsided, this tableau of birth, life, and death was strangely soothing.
Gazing past her quick, noisy audience, the petrified mother seemed
at peace with her plight. She had, after all, attained what eludes the
most disciplined yogis and roshis: perfect stillness, perfect silence.*

John Horgan

BODY

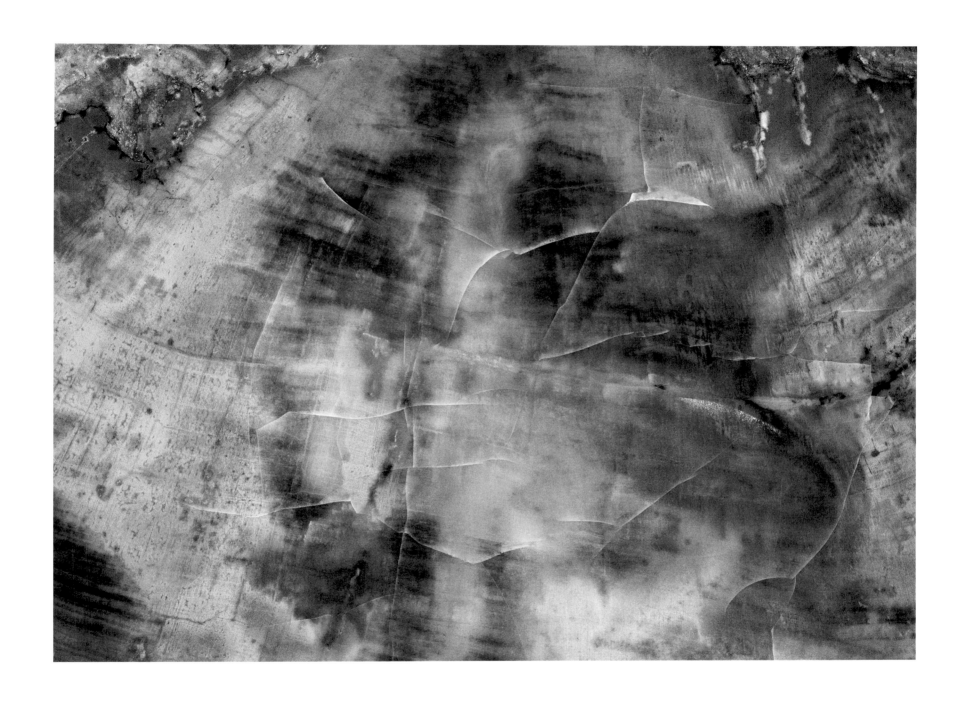

PETRIFIED WOOD

TIGER'S EYE

On a sun-crazed veldt I see you,
creeping shadow, as you steal
among grazing sheep and dozy natives,
and a golden-red aurora
flares in the distance, shooting up
lustrous flames from the scalp-land.

Alive in your haunches,
shoulders roll and paws nurse
dry earth, as I inhale three aromas:
sweet sheep, salt men, lambs
already licorice in my mouth.

Sunrise, mindrise, I begin to wake,
heart darting for cover.
My scalp feels singed.
But there are no tigers.
Only the auroras were real.
One eyelid slowly opens
to a gold blur and the purr
of morning sun on my eyebrows.

Still embroidering dreams,
my other eye gapes wide
at a tiger eye staring back,
its amber disk streaked with fire
and one emotion: death feeds.

The carnage that follows
is intimate but not personal.
Afterwards, what remains is earth,
bone, ocher, blood, the auroras bending
from scalp to sky, and just maybe
a lone flamingo pinking by.

Diane Ackerman

ANIMAL

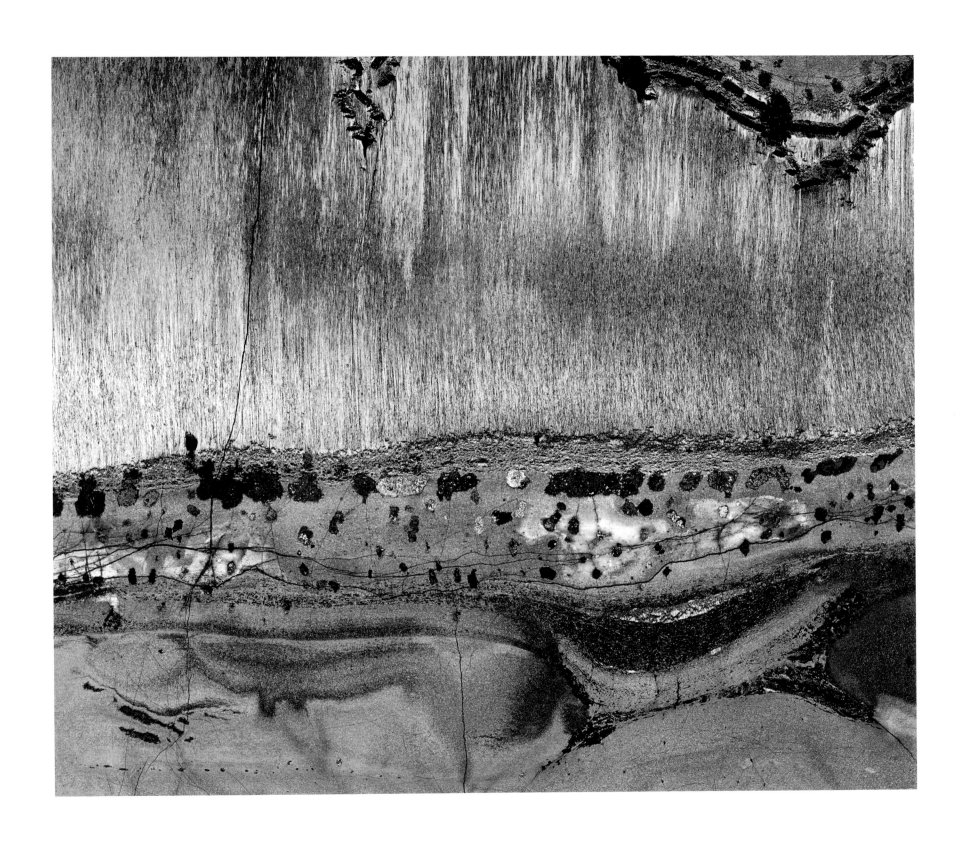

MARRA MAMBA TIGER'S-EYE

I see the iridescent feathers of a giant bird, pale violet until its great crash into the side of a black cavern, or mountain, which has compromised its beauty in the mangle of its own splayed blood. Related perhaps to the archaeopteryx, or the pterodactyl, to Icarus and Daedalus and all who once soared, or who will once again. It is fitting that the site of this catastrophe is in Siberia, scene of bitter cold and gulag prisons, and birthplace of shamans. The sphinx in its purple haze, the burnt phoenix between births, the griffon and hippogriff and their heirs may all be so much mythological hot air. Coleridge distinguished between imagination as fancy, which reaches and projects, and imagination as insight, which is the real thing, perception in the widest mode. It is fun to add the suffix "ite" to your name, and thereby to see how you would be called if you were a mineral.

Dorion Sagan

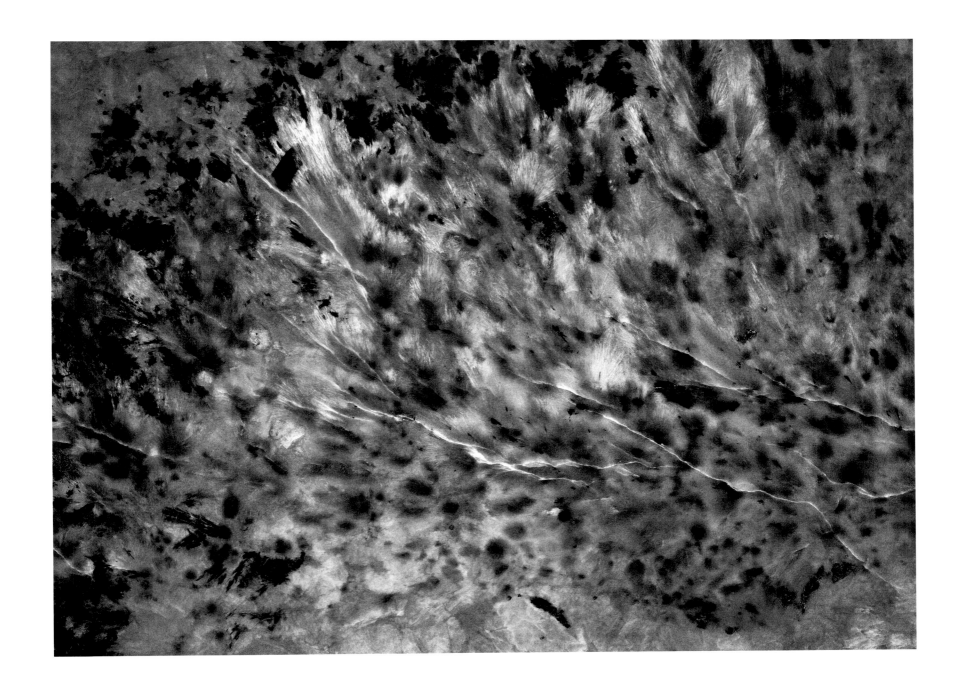

CHAROITE

Somewhere in Earth's recycled memories, unwritten even in oldest stone, there was a moment (perhaps holy, perhaps wholly random) when chemistry and geology and physics conspired to produce something new.

Not crystal growth. Not change of state. Not reaction or eruption.

A vital force burst forth, casting a glow like the Firebird of Russian lore, fighting the inexorable pull of maximum entropy—propagating and evolving, ultimately comprehending its own improbability and glorious futility, yet pushing forward still.

Andrew Revkin

ANIMAL

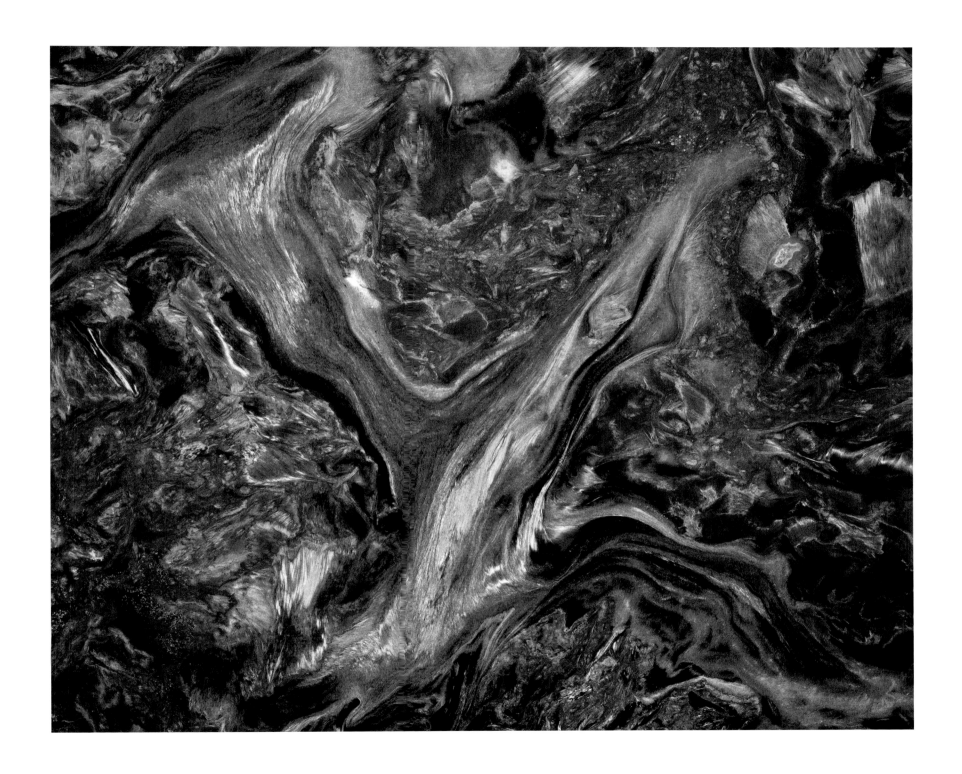

PIETERSITE

If moths' wings crumble to the touch, this rock is a landed butterfly,
its deep blue veins trumping the ocean abyss and Earth seen from a
million miles away in space. Indeed the blue is so concentrated that it
shames sapphire, scoffing at the blue china of aesthetes, its message
written in azure on blue paper and thrown overboard in blue bottles
from the blind boats of suicidal lepidopterists. Here is a blue that calls
Death out onto the carpet, making his pallid old face blush with the
embarrassment of youth. As the lover sings, "Sugar, sugar, how'd you
get so fly?" The answer, of course, is by being eaten. Some flowers
float in midair. Nectars buzz and sting. Fruit and cattle look out the
eyes of man. But chrysocolla is just copper ore.

Dorion Sagan

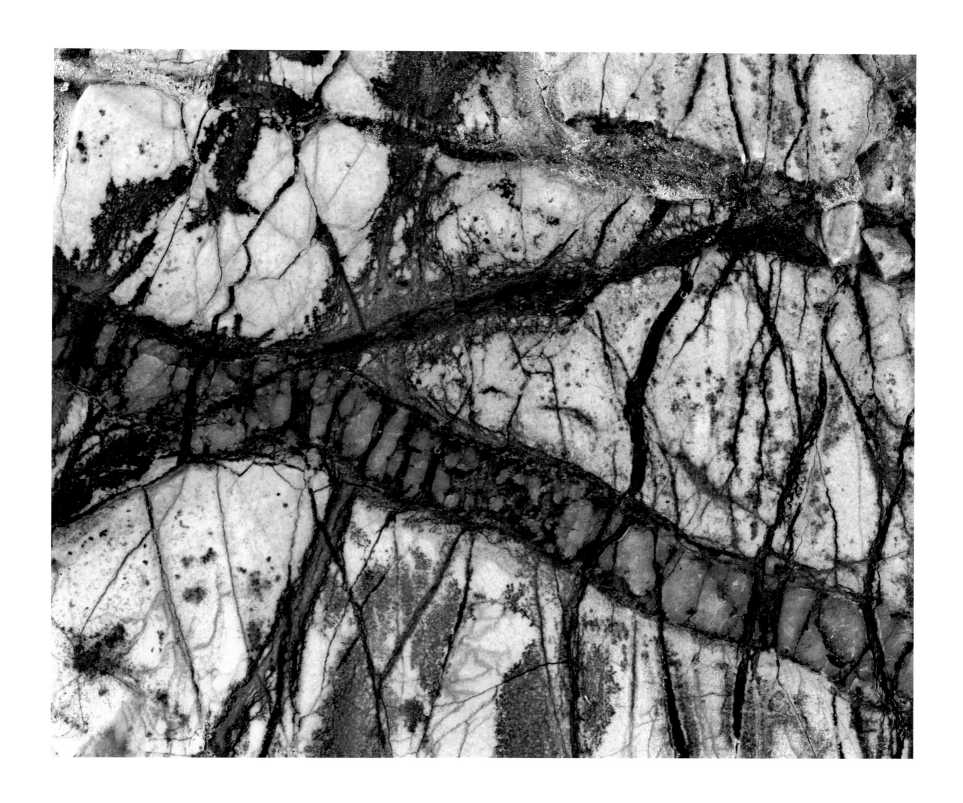

CHRYSOCOLLA

When the universe was young, there were no heavier elements
such as silicon, aluminum or calcium, so no matter such as this
stone was possible. The stuff of almost all that we see or put hand to
was cooked in the hellish hearts of stars in their unimaginable fiery
and violent explosions into supernovas. Much, much later, here
on earth, out of its fiery and molten heart, minerals crystallized.
Who could not wonder how atoms know how to combine into
silicates and calcites and other beautiful things? Where do the laws
of physics and chemistry really come from? How does matter know
how to make us? Is it really all just an accident?

This photo might be of a stone or a flower or a butterfly's wing.
It recalls the iris of the eye that beholds it. These glorious golds
and beautiful blues, blue inside blue, the color of the twilight sky,
the mystic's color and the color that conceals the essence of all color—
in this I find the wonder of another question that is the sum of all the
others: why are things so beautiful? And the beginning of an answer
as well: if they weren't, what would be the point of it all?

David Zindell

ANIMAL

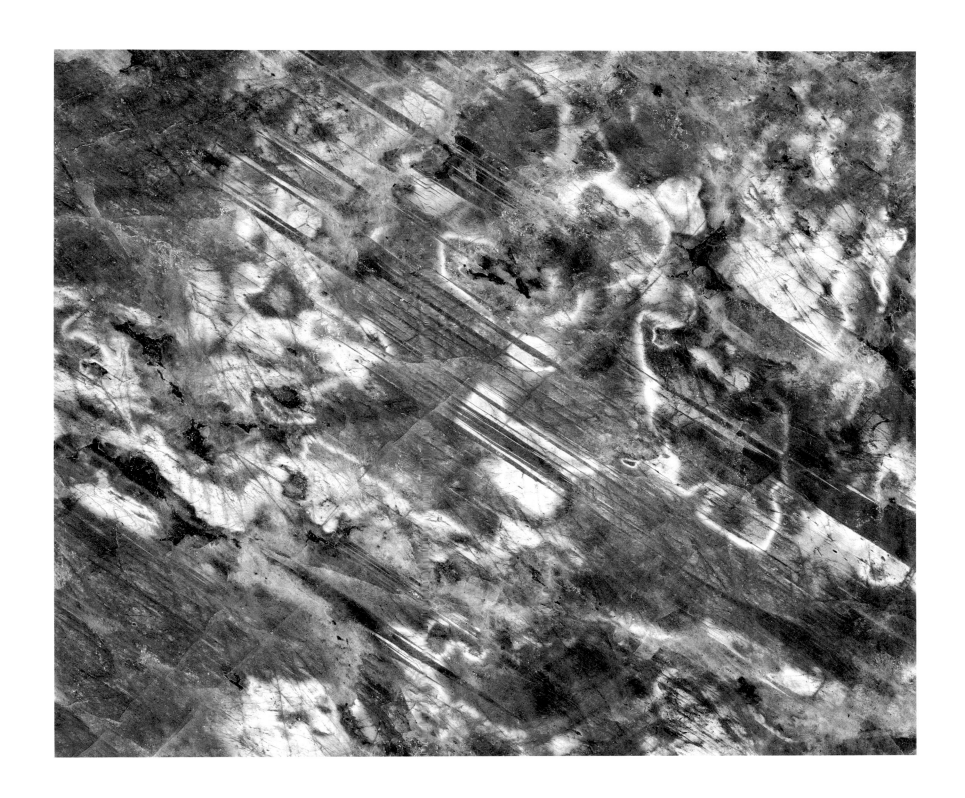

LABRADORITE

PETROGLYPH HAIKUS

Trailing crumbs of fire,
a wolf of insight steals an
electric blue heart.

Canary buried
in shale flies westward, angling
for a purer gold.

Who painted the Earth
with flat tornadoes blazing
below our cold feet?

Oh granite, finite
vaults of ingenious rock,
come ignite my eyes.

Diane Ackerman

BEAUTY

PIETERSITE

The Problem of Beauty

*It seems so … excessive, wonders such as this locked inside mere
stones. And for every marvel made manifest, infinitudes of others
remain forever unwitnessed. This surfeit of beauty should stump
scientific materialists, atheists, utilitarians, no-nonsense sorts. In*
Dreams of a Final Theory, *hardheaded physicist Steven Weinberg
rejects God as preposterous; the world is too hurtful, unfair, to be
created by the loving, just Lord the Bible postulates. The shoal against
which all theologies founder: the problem of evil. Weinberg confesses,
however, that "sometimes nature seems more beautiful than strictly
necessary." Just as evil should haunt believers in a beneficent deity,
so beauty should nag skeptics. After all, beauty, unlike evil, is not
confined to the human sphere but suffuses every micro nook and
macro cranny in the universe. If there is a Creator, perhaps He
cares only for beauty. Human suffering may be just another hue
in the divine palette. The question remains: Are we expendable, or
necessary? Our best hope is that God, narcissist that He is, needs to
hear us ooh and ahh in aesthetic delight as well as in pain.*

John Horgan

BOULDER OPAL

Again I see that beauty has no mercy. This can be a problem. The beauty can be a lure. Keats insisted on the identity of beauty and truth. Plato held beauty, truth, and the good up as ultimate ideals. The French revolution went him one worse, raising up liberty, fraternity, and equality. But equality and liberty are not equals. Freedom means also the freedom to be better, more truthful, more beautiful than one's fellows. Ergo envy, and that Franco-American bastard, political correctness, which began as an ironic liberal joke but soon metamorphosed, like the Ku Klux Klan (also originally a joke), into something deadly serious. Call it the Bergeron effect, after the hapless sap in the Vonnegut story who is too smart to be equal, and so is outfitted by the state with a special helmet that pounds his head, thereby achieving the state goal of socially acceptable equality. One need not be a neocon. But if liberty and equality are ungainly bedfellows, fated to fail as rhetoric ebbs, so that older, more regal pair, beauty and truth, also have their problems. I think of Charles Bukowski, the dirty old man whose father made him mow the lawn, preventing him from going to town to complete his homework assignment, an essay on the President's local visit. His essay was so good that the teacher read it aloud to the class. Afterwards, however, she called him over and he admitted he had made it up. That was when he said he realized what they want, "beautiful lies." The rest of his life was devoted to telling the ugly truth.

Dorion Sagan

BEAUTY

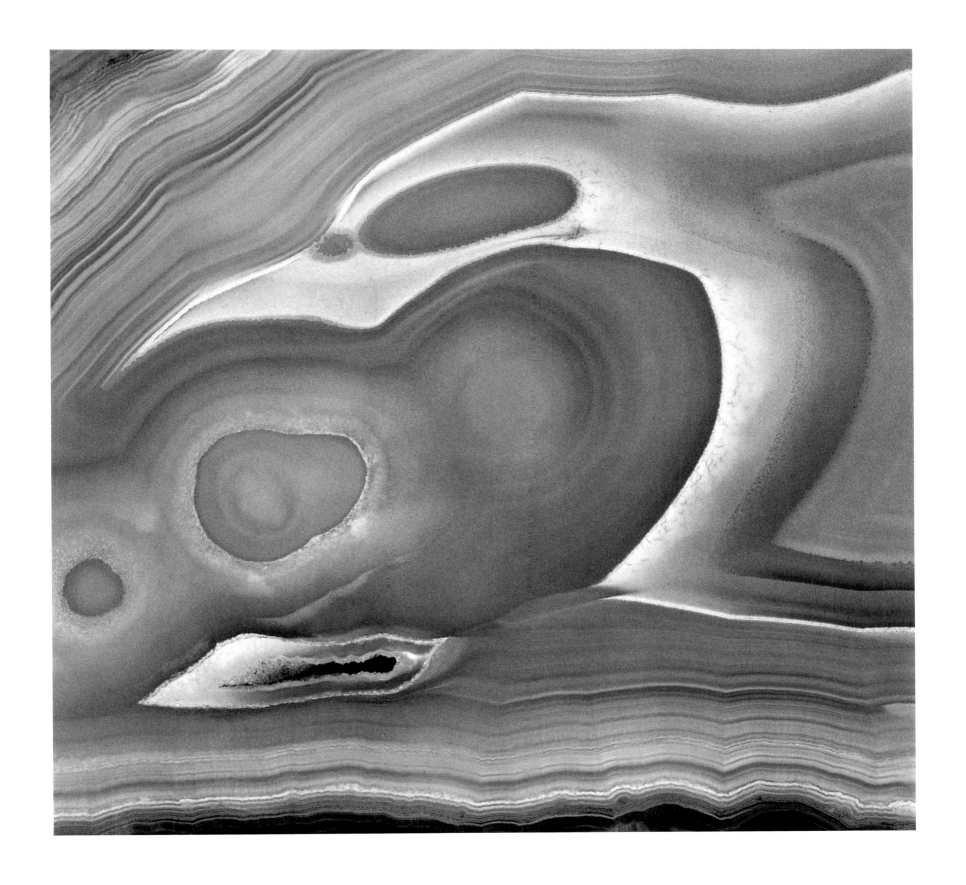

BANDED AGATE

BEYOND THE STONE

That is the labor of the jasper or the agate.

It lays itself down

patiently and permanently;

it never asks to know its own design.

From where we stand,

beyond the stones,

we see patterns they cannot.

A crystal lattice forms an egg.

A clump of iron forms a flame.

If these minerals, in their blindness,

were allowed to make such beauty,

why not assume that we

have been allowed to make our own?

Laura Atkinson

DENDRITIC AGATE

Rock Descriptions

Si & Ann Frazier and Robert Hutchinson

Each rock specimen shown in this book is labeled with the most common name under which it is sold in the gemrock trade. In general, a specimen's trade name is not the same as the approved name assigned to it in scientific classification. In the descriptive paragraphs that follow, trade names are distinguished by quotation marks and translated into standard scientific names. For the sake of clarity, the profusion of synonymous trade names is ignored. Technical terms are usually defined (often in parentheses) in each description as they occur. Italicized page numbers given at the end of some descriptions refer to other specimens with the same trade name whose descriptions amplify the description of the cross-referenced specimen. Each title is followed by an italicized magnification factor (e.g., *3x*), giving the linear scale of the main photograph relative to the rock itself. Beneath each title, the specimen's provenance is given in nested form (as in *locality, county, state, nation*).

PAGE 13
PETRIFIED WOOD *2.5x*
Near Petrified Forest National Park,
Apache County, Arizona, USA

Petrified wood is a variety of jasper (opaque to subtranslucent chalcedony or microcrystalline quartz) formed by permineralization and replacement (see below) of wood tissue by silica (SiO_2) precipitated from silica-rich aqueous solution (one in which water is the solvent). The petrified wood logs and chips strewn across the 93,492-acre Petrified Forest National Park and its vicinity are broken sections of fallen trunks of 215-million-year-old conifer trees whose tissue was permineralized and replaced by microcrystalline quartz precipitated out of silica-rich solutions that infiltrated the wood soon after its burial in a floodplain environment. Groundwater, saturated with silica in solution derived from silica-rich volcanic ash and tuffaceous sandstone (sandstone containing abundant volcanic ash), impregnated the buried tree trunks. The silica-rich solution in the waterlogged trunks underwent dehydration to silica gel and petrification to microcrystalline quartz almost immediately, on the order of tens to hundreds of years. Petrification of wood is in general separable into two stages: permineralization and replacement. In permineralization, pore spaces in the original wood are filled with microcrystalline quartz and the original cell structure remains visible under a microscope. In replacement, the remaining organic matter in the wood is completely replaced by quartz, in result of which replacement fossils show no cell structure under a microscope. The specimen in the photograph is mostly replaced but retains traces of its original quarter grain. *See also pp. 17, 117, 135, and 137.*

PAGE 15
OCEAN JASPER *3x*
Near Marovato, Ambolobozo District,
Mahajanga Province, Madagascar

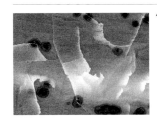

"Ocean jasper" is a trade name for a particular variety of orbicular jasper that is characterized by uniquely rich arrays of white, pink, green, red, and yellow colors; of orbicular configurations ranging from solitary and binary individuals to planar or botryoidal aggregates; and of individual orbicules ranging in size and morphology from small homogeneous spheroids to large intricately nested shells, sometimes encased in drusy coronas. The specimen in the photograph shows a solitary and binary configuration of large ellipsoidal orbicules composed of weakly differentiated shells. "Ocean jasper" has been available on the world market only since the 2000 Tucson Gem and Mineral Show, to which Paul Obenich brought samples from his claim on a remote section of the coast of northwest Madagascar. A single specimen of this unique orbicular jasper from Madagascar had found its way the Musée de Minéralogie in Paris in the 1950s, but its provenance on the island was unknown. A young Frenchman admired it then and resolved someday to find its source. In 1998, Paul Obenich, now in his seventies, undertook a systematic search of the coastline of the Mahajanga Basin of Madagascar and eventually discovered the source—a rock outcrop, measuring just 150 feet by 100 feet in an intertidal zone where it is submerged except at low tide. The outcrop can only be mined by hand at daytime low tide and is in a district without roads, so that the mined material must be carried out by boat. *See also pp. 35, 83, and 99.*

PAGE 17
PETRIFIED WOOD *2.5x*
Near Petrified Forest National Park,
Apache County, Arizona, USA

Petrified wood is a variety of jasper formed by permineralization and replacement of wood tissue by silica precipitated from silica-rich aqueous solution. The specimen in the photograph is permineralized, meaning that the original cell structure remains visible. In cross section (perpendicular to the length of the trunk), it displays annual rings and radial cracks relict from the living tree trunk of 215 million years ago. In *Micrographia* (1665), Robert Hooke, the first scientist to compare petrified wood with organic wood under a microscope, inferred correctly that "this petrify'd Wood having lain in some place where it was well soak'd with petrifying water (that is, such water as is well impregnated with stony and earthy particles) did by degrees separate abundance of stony particles from the permeating water, which stony particles, being by means of the fluid vehicle convey'd, not onely into the Microscopical pores but also into the pores or Interstitia of that part of the Wood, which through the Microscope, appears most solid." The "stony particles from the permeating water" that petrified the wood of Petrified Forest National Park generally included, in addition to quartz, disseminations of various metal oxides and ions that lend their characteristic colors to the transparent-to-translucent whitish-bluish base complexion of the quartz. Ferric oxide (hematite) imbues the quartz with red; iron hydroxide (goethite), yellow and buff; chromium ions, green; cobalt ions, blue. Petrified logs that contain organic traces have carbon-dark features, such as those in the photograph. *See also pp. 13, 117, 135, and 137.*

PAGE 19
FUCHSITE *2.5x*
Spanish Peaks, Madison Range,
Madison County, Montana, USA

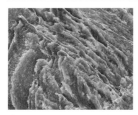

"Fuchsite" is an obsolete name for chromphyllite, also known as *chromian muscovite*—one of twelve varietal species in the muscovite subgroup of the mica group in the phyllosilicates class. The chemical formula for chromphyllite is $(K,Ba)(Cr,Al)_2(AlSi_3)O_{10}(OH,F)_2$. Chromphyllite contains as much as 4.8 percent chromium oxide (Cr_2O_3). Ionic chromium (Cr^{3+}) is the chromophore (transition metal that gives color to a mineral by virtue of the characteristic energy shifts of its outer valence electrons) that imparts to chromphyllite its emerald green color. As do all the varieties of muscovite, chromphyllite has perfect cleavage in one direction, translucent diaphaneity, and a micaceous (platy) habit. The specimen in the photograph has been cut obliquely to the cleavage plane, so that the edges of the parallel mica sheets appear serried. Muscovite was so named in 1850 by the father of American mineralogy, James Dwight Dana (1813-1895), who happens to be the great-great-granduncle of William Dana Atkinson, who took the photograph. Dana named muscovite after "Muscovy glass," a term prevalent since the sixteenth century for sheets of mica employed as window, lantern, and stove panes. The specimen in the photograph is from Archean quartzite in the northwestern part of the Madison Range in southwestern Montana. Some of the ridge-forming quartzite in the Spanish Peaks displays aventurescence—a green glimmer caused by reflectance from chromphyllite inclusions. In the neighboring Tobacco Root Mountains, chromphyllite is found in the gangue (non-economic rock hosting an economic mineral) of ruby, whose red color also comes from chromium.

PAGE 21
PIETERSITE *4x*
Farm Hopewell No. 204,
Outjo District, Kunene Region, Namibia

Pietersite is the microgranular quartz end-product of a complex metamorphic history that ran through four precursory forms. Pietersite is a fault breccia, most of the constituents of which are hawk's-eye and/or tiger's-eye. Fault breccia is any rock composed of angular fragments, disaggregated by crushing, grinding, and shearing along a fault. The precursor of the breccia is hawk's-eye and/or tiger's-eye—which are genetically-related but color-distinguished members of a silica-replacement series, with blue/green hawk's-eye being the precursor of yellow/brown tiger's-eye. The precursor of hawk's-eye is crocidolite (also called "blue asbestos"), which is the asbestiform form of riebeckite. The precursor of crocidolite is massive riebeckite, which is an alkali amphibole also distinguished by its blue color. Crocidolite occurs in metamorphic banded iron formations in southern Africa and Western Australia, in seams conformable with bedding. Crocidolite accounts for four percent of world production of asbestos. The transformation of massive riebeckite—$Na_2(Fe,Mg)_3Fe_2Si_8O_{22}(OH)_2$—to crocidolite occurred when riebeckite beds in banded iron formations were subjected to shearing stress. The transformation of crocidolite to hawk's-eye occurred by permeation or partial replacement of closely packed parallel crocidolite fibers by microcrystalline quartz. The transformation of hawk's-eye to tiger's-eye occurred by the alteration of crocidolite fibers to hydrous iron oxide and by partial or complete replacement of the hawk's-eye by microcrystalline quartz pseudomorphs. The transformation of hawk's-eye and/or tiger's-eye to pietersite occurred by brecciation as the silicified crocidolite seam was subjected to further shearing stress. *See also pp. 75, 95, 105, 143, and 149.*

PAGE 23
SODALITE *3x*
Swartbooisdrift area, Kaokoland District,
Kunene Region, Namibia

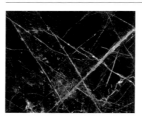

Sodalite is a feldspathoid tectosilicate named for its high sodium content—for sodium accounts for almost 25 weight percent of the mineral ($Na_8Al_6Si_6O_{24}Cl_2$). Sodalite shares with lapis lazuli, which also belongs to the sodalite group, its deep azure blue color, its vitreous luster, and its cage-like aluminosilicate structure for housing big chlorine anions. Sodalite is a comparatively rare mineral that occurs in alkali-rich igneous rocks, in association with other feldspathoid minerals such as nepheline and cancrinite. The specimen in the photograph comes from the Kunene Intrusive Complex, a nine-mile-thick dome of alkali-rich magma that intruded into the granitic country rock of northern Namibia 1.4 billion years ago. Transformation of the granitic country rock by contact with carbonatite magma (magma of largely carbonate composition) injected into dykes cutting through the Swartbooisdrift area produced, as part of a chemical process called *fenitization*, the Swartbooisdrift sodalite deposit. The fracture lines traversing the specimen in the photograph are traces of the sodalite's poor dodecahedral cleavage. Some of the fractures are pointed with orange-colored cancrinite, a carbonate mineral that is susceptible to attack even by weak acids in rainwater. This susceptibility can be avoided in decorative outdoor stone paneling by using a ceramic sodalite simulant.

PAGE 25
DENDRITIC OPALITE *3x*
Norseman, Dundas Shire,
Goldfields-Esperance Region,
Western Australia, Australia

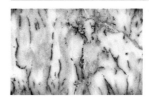

"Dendritic opalite" is a varietal trade name for an opaque or feebly translucent variety of common opal (opal lacking the "play of color" that characterizes precious opal) containing a minor amount of alumina and dendritic veinlets. Its color may be bluish-white, yellow, or red. The play of color in precious opal is caused by its internal structure: submicroscopically minute, densely packed, equigranular spheres of amorphous silica, immersed in a watery bath of silica gel. Gem quality opals are composed of silica spheres of homogeneous size, regularly packed in an ordered array. Common opal—such as the specimen in the photograph—is composed of spheres of heterogeneous size and relatively disordered arrangement. The specimen in the photograph, from Norseman in Western Australia, appears to be a re-cemented brecciated opalite: locally colored blue by diffusion from the manganese oxide and hydroxide material lodged in an early family of subparallel healed cracks; and elsewhere colored yellow by disseminated iron hydroxides related to a later family of cracks, oblique to the first. Norseman sits in the Archean greenstone belt at the southeastern edge of the Yilgarn craton, which contains rocks dated to 4.2 billion years. The gold, nickel, tantalum, and gypsum deposits of Norseman bear witness to the complex history of deformation and hydrothermal alteration undergone by the rocks of Norseman. *See also pp. 107, 113, 121, and 151.*

PLUME AGATE *2x*
Graveyard Point,
Malheur County, Oregon, USA

"Plume agate" is an example of an agate (a translucent chalcedony or cryptocrystalline quartz) that is not banded but is rather a variety of "moss agate" (an agate with variously splotched areas, commonly arborescent in shape). "Plume agate" is distinguished by sporadic fluffy-looking masses, some of which resemble egret plumes. In the specimen in the photograph, reddish brown, yellow, yellowish brown, and white plumes and blackish and gray-brown dendrites are contained in blue agate. The specimen comes from the Graveyard Point sill, a 500-foot-thick differentiated basaltic intrusion covering eight square miles of southeastern Oregon near the Idaho border. The Graveyard Point intrusion—named for the pioneer cemetery next to it—erupted 8 million years ago during the Late Miocene into Middle Miocene onto silicic tuffs at the border between the Snake River Plain and the Basin and Range province. The intrusion is pervasively cut by granophyre dykes and by veins. The veins, varying in width from one inch to two feet, are mostly vertical in orientation and composed of "plume agate." Both the plumes and the dendrites project perpendicularly from the vein walls toward the center of the vein. As the intrusion cooled, cracks formed in it that served as passages for silica-rich late-magmatic and hydrothermal fluids. These cracks were progressively filled by agate growing inward from the walls toward the center planes of the cracks. The resultant veins are either completely closed, in which case a plane of rough bilateral symmetry marks the center of the vein, as in the case of the specimen in the photograph; or incompletely closed. According to Graveyard Point miner, Eugene Mueller, the central voids of his incompletely closed "plume agate" seams are lined with what he calls "angel-wing chalcedony"—which seems from his photographs likely to be a silica pseudomorph after acicular goethite. Mueller infers from field relations that the plumose structure in the agate is a pentimento of stalactitic "angel wings" growing inward from the vein walls. The yellow and reddish brown colors of the plumes are consistent with the hypothesis of precursory acicular goethite. Also consistent is the observation that "plume agate" undercuts easily because the plume is softer than the blue agate. The blackish dendritic structures in the photograph are manganese oxides and hydroxides.

BLUE CALCITE *3x*
Mapimí, Durango, Mexico

Coarsely crystalline blue calcite commonly occurs in skarn deposits, which form in the hydrothermal contact aureoles of igneous bodies intruded into limestone—as in the case of the Mapimí deposit, from which the specimen in the photograph comes. In some skarn deposits, such as the one quarried into Sky Blue Hill in Riverside County, California, blue calcite is so plentiful that it is used for road metal, sugar refining, and Portland cement. The upper-left corner of the specimen in the photograph illustrates two of calcite's characteristic properties. The prismatic colors among the closely packed parallel edges are a result of calcite's extreme birefringence, which is the splitting of light traversing a transparent crystal into two beams traveling at different speeds. The parallel edges themselves display calcite's perfect rhombohedral cleavage. Calcite has three directions of perfect cleavage, corresponding to the three pairs of faces on a rhombohedron (a solid bounded by six oblique-angled parallelograms). The specimen of calcite in the photograph is highly sheared. The blue color of blue calcite is produced by natural ionizing irradiation of sheared calcite.

CRAZY LACE AGATE *3x*
Sierra Santa Lucia,
Chihuahua, Mexico

"Crazy lace agate" is a varietal trade name for an agate (a translucent chalcedony or cryptocrystalline quartz) that is distinguished by multicolored and twisting bands—both concentric and fortification (polygonal with salients and re-entrants) in style—and that is mined from veins in limestone of the Sierra Santa Lucia in the Mexican states of Chihuahua and Durango. "Crazy lace agate" is significantly more permeable than Brazilian agate, allowing it to be dyed loud colors with aniline dyes. The specimen in the photograph, showing as it does numerous bands of pale gray and white, which are intrinsic pseudo-colors of unadulterated chalcedony, is all-natural in color. *See also pp. 79 and 89.*

BOTSWANA AGATE *4x*
Bobonong area, Central District, Botswana

"Botswana agate" is a banded agate (a translucent chalcedony or cryptocrystalline quartz) that is distinguished by asymmetrical concentric banding and that is mined in the Bobonong area of Botswana. "Botswana agate" formed in amygdules (gas cavities) in basaltic lava flows that were extruded at the top of the Karoo Sequence in the Middle Jurassic epoch 180 million years ago, in connection with the initial rifting phase of the break-up of Gondwana. The amygdules in the lavas were initially filled with hydrosol (a colloidal system in which water is the dispersion medium for silica polymers) under high internal pressure. The hydrosol then dehydrated into silica gel, which in turn crystallized and coated the walls of the amygdule concentrically and centripetally, imitating the shape of the original cavity. The banding of the "Botswana agate" in the photograph is inferred to have lost its symmetry after banding but prior to complete crystallization of the silica gel into chalcedony—perhaps as a result of disturbance or depressurization associated with renewed lava effusion. The banding of the specimen in the photograph is pale gray, bluish gray, grayish white, and milky white. All of these hues are intrinsic pseudo-colors of chalcedony that depend not on compositional differences but on the diffusive effects of variations in the quantity and size of micropores in and among the microfibers making up the chalcedony of each agate band. "Botswana agate" was a staple of the agate market in the 1960s and '70s but has become harder to find in recent decades. *See also pp. 119 and 153.*

PAGE 35
OCEAN JASPER 3x
Near Marovato, Ambolobozo District,
Mahajanga Province, Madagascar

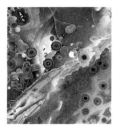

"Ocean jasper" is a trade name for a particular variety of orbicular jasper that is characterized by uniquely rich arrays of orbicules in a variety of colors, configurations, sizes, and morphologies. The specimen in the photograph shows a botryoidal (shaped like a cluster of grapes) configuration of large spheroidal orbicules composed of intricately nested shells. "Ocean jasper" comes from a single bed in a single locality near the fishing village of Marovato on the northwestern coast of Madagascar, in the Mahajanga Basin. The "ocean jasper" bed is a flow-banded rhyolite that was laid down 90 million years ago and which has since undergone complete silicification (replacement by silica). It occurs as an ashfall deposit sandwiched between basalt flows. The Marovato suite is a member of the thick sequence of west-dipping Cretaceous volcanics in the Mahajanga Basin, erupted during the early phase of rifting of the Indian subcontinent from Madagascar. By this time, Madagascar had already reached its present position 250 miles east of the coast of Africa. The Late Cretaceous rifting episode that left Madagascar docked to the edge of the African plate is recorded by symmetrical flood basalts in northern Madagascar and in the Western Ghats of India. *See also pp. 15, 83, and 99.*

PAGE 37
RED JASPER 2x
Northern California, USA

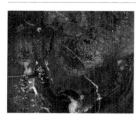

The monochromatic red color of this jasper (opaque-to-subtranslucent chalcedony or microcrystalline quartz) is from disseminated hematite. Later blebs of colorless milky white chalcedony can be seen to have infiltrated brittle cracks and pods of textural disruption in the jasper.

PAGE 39
CHRYSOCOLLA 2.5x
Ray Mine, Hot Tamale Peak,
Mineral Creek District,
Pinal County, Arizona, USA

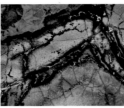

Virtually all gemrocks called "chrysocolla" in the marketplace—including the specimen in the photograph—are in fact composed in large part of silica, in the form of either quartz or chalcedony, intermixed with and impregnating various secondary copper minerals, among which the mineral chrysocolla, distinguished by its diverse blue to greenish blue hues, is significant as a coloring agent. The mineral chrysocolla, a hydrous copper silicate, has a Mohs hardness of 1.5 to 3.5 and is too fragile and friable for lapidary work. Chalcedony has a hardness of 6.5 to 7 and takes a good polish. "Chrysocolla" (the gemrock) has a hardness intermediate between chrysocolla (the mineral) and chalcedony, such that it can be polished if first coated with an epoxy resin. Chrysocolla (the mineral) ranges in color from bright blue to sky blue to sea green to emerald green and is often pseudomorphous after other crystals. "Chrysocolla" (the rock) displays a mélange of colors in the same specimen, including blue, green, yellow, brown, and black. The name *chrysocolla* (from Greek for "gold glue") is first encountered in the treatise *On Stones* (*c.* 315 B.C.) of Theophrastus, who alluded to it as a mineral from Cyprus (the name of the island itself meaning "copper") used as an ingredient in gold solder. Adding copper to gold in small proportions has the effect of deepening the yellow color in gold, lowering its melting point, and significantly increasing its hardness and tensile strength. All of the colors in the specimen in the photograph are contributed by various compounds of copper that formed in the oxidation zone of the copper deposit that is exploited by the Ray Mine. The bright blue is from the hydrous copper silicate, chrysocolla; the green is from the hydrous copper carbonate, malachite; the yellow-green might be from hydrous copper arsenate, conichalite; the black fracture filling is the copper oxide, tenorite. *See also pp. 43, 67, and 145.*

PAGE 41
OWYHEE PICTURE JASPER 4x
Owyhee Uplands between Owyhee Reservoir
and Three Fingers Rock,
Malheur County, Oregon, USA

"Owyhee picture jasper" is a specific trade name for a silicified rhyolitic tuff characterized by distinctive ochre and yellow patterns on a pale blue ground that is mined from three claims located within a mile of each other, above 4,000 feet in the Owyhee Uplands of Oregon. The "Owyhee picture jasper" ashfall tuff belongs to the Owyhee Rhyolite unit, erupted 11 million years ago from the Steens Mountains, one hundred miles to the southwest. The volcanism of the Owyhee Uplands in the Late Miocene and Early Pliocene was bimodal, such that the iron-lacking Owyhee Rhyolite is sandwiched by iron-rich basalts. Ions from the basalts mobilized by hydrothermal solutions were precipitated along cracks in the tuff as ochre hydrohematite and yellow goethite. Flow-banding in the tuff in the lower half of the photograph can also be seen to exert control on the arrangement of the colors. *See also p. 101.*

PAGE 43
CHRYSOCOLLA 3x
Morenci Mine, Clifton-Morenci District,
Greenlee County, Arizona, USA

"Chrysocolla" (the rock) is composed in large part of silica intermixed with and impregnating various secondary copper minerals, among which the mineral chrysocolla is one. All of the colors in the specimen in the photograph are contributed by various compounds of copper that formed in the oxidation zone of the copper deposit that is exploited by the vast open pit of Morenci Mine. The bright blue is from the hydrous copper silicate, chrysocolla; the green is from the hydrous copper carbonate, malachite; the black bodies are the copper oxide, tenorite; the buff portions represent chalcedony lacking in copper-bearing disseminations; the green line flecked with white cutting across the bottom of the photograph is a quartz vein bearing malachite. *See also pp. 39, 67, and 145*

PAGE 45
MORRISONITE *2.5x*
Morrison Ranch, Owyhee River Canyon,
Malheur County, Oregon, USA

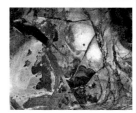

"Morrisonite" is a specific trade name for a variegated jasper found at a single locality in the Owyhee Uplands of southeastern Oregon. It is a silicified rhyolitic welded tuff that is characterized by a distinctive assemblage of red, yellow, green and blue-green "pastel-on-glass" colors and that is mined from five claims located on the southeastern edge of the thousand-foot-deep Owyhee River canyon, two miles upstream of the southern end of Owyhee Reservoir. The "morrisonite" is found amid veins filling brecciated tuff in pinnacles rising through the colluvium of the canyon cliffs. The "morrisonite" rhyolitic tuff is roughly contemporaneous with the 11-million-year-old "Owyhee picture jasper" rhyolitic tuff, 25 miles to the northeast—both deriving from the rhyolitic eruptions in the Steens Mountains 11 million years ago. The "morrisonite" tuff differs from the "Owyhee picture jasper" tuff in being welded, which means that the glassy volcaniclastic fragments were hot enough to fuse into a mass. The "morrisonite" tuff also differs from the "Owyhee picture jasper" tuff in being brecciated, which means that it was broken up into coarse angular fragments by grinding in a fault zone. Wide pull-aparts between breccia fragments in the left half of the photograph can be seen to have been filled with colorless chalcedony (microcrystalline quartz). Many other cracks and tension gashes in the photograph have likewise been sealed with colored chalcedony, dividing the "morrisonite" into polygonal compartments. *See also p. 131.*

PAGE 47
PICASSO MARBLE *2x*
Minersville area, Mineral Mountains,
Beaver County, Utah, USA

"Picasso marble" is a specific trade name for a distinctively patterned carbonate rock that is quarried in the Minersville area of southwestern Utah from a forty-foot-wide stockwork in gray limestone, pervaded by diversely oriented transecting veinlets and variously colored by the passage of hydrothermal fluids associated with magmatic activity. The specimen in the photograph exhibits two generations of veinlets: the older dark veinlets, such as the ones crisscrossing the light gray limestone body on the left with the resorbed border; and younger veinlets of sparry white calcite filling fracture planes along which differential movement has taken place. *See also p. 53.*

PAGE 49
CHAROITE *3x*
Sirenevyi Kamen Deposit, Maly Murun Massif,
Olekmo-Charskoye Upland, Sakha Republic, Russia

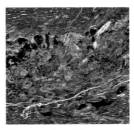

The mineral charoite is a hydrated inosilicate of lilac color. It was identified as a new mineral in 1978 and comes from only one locality in the world: the Sirenevyi Kamen (Russian for "lilac stone") charoite deposit in the southern fenitized aureole of the Maly Murun massif, on the divide between the Tokko and Chara Rivers 140 miles southwest of the town of Olekminsk on the Lena River. Charoite is named after the Chara River, even though the Sirenevyi Kamen deposit is actually in the Tokko River watershed and forty miles distant from the Chara. The Murun alkaline-syenite igneous massif was intruded during the Mesozoic into the Upper Proterozoic sedimentary cover of the Siberian Platform. Charoite occurs as segregated pods and veins in intensely fractured sandstones that were metasomatically altered by contact with porphyry dykes injected into the wall rock in the final stage of the emplacement of the Murun massif. Charoite is one of five new mineral species found exclusively in the Murun massif—the others being tinaksite, davanite, tokkoite, and murunite. In the specimen in the photograph, the black areas are aegerine, the brownish-gray ovoids enclosing prismatic shadows are altered microcline feldspars, and the orangey-brown splotches are tinaksite. *See also pp. 111 and 141.*

PAGE 51
DENDRITIC SOAPSTONE *4x*
Near Cameron,
Madison County, Montana, USA

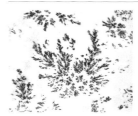

Soapstone, also called steatite (from Greek for "fat rock"), is a metamorphic rock of massive or schistose texture with a soft unctuous feel and waxy luster, composed essentially of talc—a hydrous magnesium silicate secondary after ferromagnesian minerals. As a phyllosilicate mineral with perfect cleavage in one direction, talc is composed of two-dimensional plates that slide readily on top of each other, imparting to soapstone its unique greasiness (you can fry eggs on a soapstone griddle without grease), softness (you can scratch it with your fingernail), and sectility (you can cut it with a knife). The specimen in the photograph comes from the only locality in the world, a quarter-mile-square outcropping in southwestern Montana, from which "dendritic soapstone" is mined. The manganese oxide dendrites (branching figures) were precipitated out of solutions that infiltrated the rock along the planes of talc cleavage. As a result, dendritic figures are revealed only in sections that are cut parallel to those planes.

PICASSO MARBLE *2x*
Minersville area, Mineral Mountains,
Beaver County, Utah, USA

"Picasso marble" is a specific trade name for a pervasively fractured carbonate rock quarried in southwestern Utah that is filled with interpenetrating veins that delivered bimodal color effects in shimmering shades of bluish gray and golden brown to the host limestone. Although the term *marble* properly refers only to metamorphosed carbonate rocks, "marble" is commonly applied in the marketplace to any predominantly carbonate rock that is compact and fine-grained enough to take a good polish. The latter is the case with "Picasso marble," which is used as a decorative stone for facing buildings in arid climates (for carbonate rock is susceptible to attack by weak acids in rainwater) and for ornaments, notably Zuni-style zoomorphic carvings and fancy knife handles. "Picasso marble" is a semi-hard gemrock, being less than 4 on the Mohs hardness scale of 10, on which agate or jasper rank around 6.5 to 7. The relative softness of Picasso marble makes it amenable to carving and polishing but unsuitable for high-impact items, such as ring-stones or floors. *See also p. 47.*

DALI STONE *1x*
Guangxi Province, China

An art form called *gong shi*—translated as "rocks to be admired"—has been practiced in China since the Tang era (A.D. 618-906). *Gong shi*—also known as "spirit stones", "scholars' stones", and "table rocks"—are admired for the microcosmic suggestiveness of their natural or subtly altered three-dimensional "found" form, unpolished except by wind, water, and meditative hand-rubbing. With the advent of modern polishing technology, connoisseurs of *gong shi* can now venture inside the stone. In the specimen in the photograph, manganese oxide/hydroxide dendrites precipitated from a mineralizing and oxidizing solution that percolated through faults and cracks in the host limestone and diffused into the fissure margins as a halo, bleaching the organic impurities in the limestone. The specimen in the photograph falls into the *gong shi* category of *dali shi*, meaning "marble stone"—often marked with an evocative mineral pattern, such as dendritic "mountains and rivers," that is best appreciated in polished blocks or domes.

POPPY JASPER *2x*
Paradise Valley, Morgan Hill,
Santa Clara County, California, USA

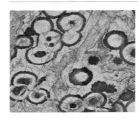

"Poppy jasper" is a trade name for a particular variety of orbicular jasper that is characterized by large (centimeter-scale), variously conjoined spheroidal and ellipsoidal orbicules. Orbicular jasper forms when rhyolitic ash (airborne fragments of volcanic eruptive material of the composition of granite, only more silica-rich) cools exceptionally quickly, perhaps in standing water. Just as big equant grains of quartz and alkali feldspar crystallize from slow-cooling granite magma, so radial aggregates of needle-like crystals of quartz and alkali feldspar under rare conditions crystallize from a fast-cooling rhyolitic ash. In the specimen in the photograph, from Morgan Hill, at the southern end of California's Silicon Valley wedged between the San Andreas and Calaveras faults, each orbicule is banded concentrically with brick-reds and yellows and enclosed in a yellow corona composed of sheaves of radially acicular yellow that merges with the coronas of its neighbors to form a yellow ground. The Morgan Hill "poppy jasper" seam is exposed on the side of Morgan Hill (now called "El Toro" by the residents of the city of Morgan Hill, to distinguish the hill from the city named after the hill), which is composed of a Cretaceous sequence of volcanic rocks. After the "poppy jasper" float on Morgan Hill became exhausted in the mid-twentieth century, a fool dynamited the seam, shattering it into fragments too small for lapidary use. As a result, the Morgan Hill variety of "poppy jasper" is represented in today's market only by recycled specimens from old collections.

BIGGS JASPER *2x*
Biggs Junction, Sherman County, Oregon, USA

"Biggs jasper" is a specific trade name for a hard silicified tuff with distinctive arcaded banding that is found in the vicinity of the town of Biggs Junction, 190 miles up the Columbia River. Most "Biggs jasper" outcrops were submerged by the filling of the pool of The Dalles Dam in 1960, but material such as that in the photograph is still quarried at the mouth of Fulton Canyon. "Biggs jasper" is an interbed of ashfall between two Miocene lava flows in the Columbia River Basalt Group, which comprises a stack of three hundred major lava flows that inundated northern Oregon, southern Washington, and western Idaho with 40,000 cubic miles of basaltic lava between 17 and 14.5 million years ago. The ash tuff that subsequently silicified into "Biggs jasper" was shed eastward as aerial ash from volcanoes of the emerging Cascade Range. The arcaded banding of "Biggs jasper" is a Liesegang phenomenon associated with the silicification ("jasperization") of the tuff. Liesegang bands form when reactants in a gel diffuse and precipitate in relation to a moving reaction boundary in an ordered way such that the concentrations of the reactants dynamically organize themselves into parallel bands within the gel. Later precipitation of manganese oxide and hydroxide dendrites occurred via the crack in the lower right corner of the photograph. Crystallites of weddellite have been discovered in cavities of "Biggs jasper." Discovered in Antarctica in 1942, weddellite is a calcium oxalate mineral that is exceedingly rare in rocks but quite common in urinary calculi and opuntia cactus.

INDIAN PAINT ROCK *5x*
Death Valley National Park,
San Bernardino County, California, USA

"Indian paint rock" is a specific trade name for a pale blue or buff Tertiary tuff from the southeastern corner of Death Valley National Park whose black-accented fractures are "painted" with broad rust-red or blood-red hematitic oxidation margins. The banding in the specimen in the photograph records successive laminar ash flows. The bands are graded in grain size, indicating the possibility that the ash was reworked by water transport. When Death Valley National Monument became a national park in 1994, collection of "Indian paint rock" from the Amargosa Wash and Owlshead Mountains became illegal. It is still legal, however, to drive off Highway 127 at the Harry Wade exit to the "Indian paint rock" fields. "Indian paint rock" is not sufficiently indurated by silica impregnation to qualify as a jasper. Although "Indian paint rock" is too soft to take a high polish, a flat finish is arguably more conducive to showing its linear pattern and earthy colors, anyway.

AMETHYST SAGE AGATE *4x*
Quinn River south of Denio,
Humboldt County, Nevada, USA

"Amethyst sage agate" is a varietal trade name for an agate (a translucent chalcedony or cryptocrystalline quartz) that is not banded but rather belongs to the informal subclass of "moss agate" (an agate with variously splotched areas, commonly arborescent in shape). "Amethyst sage agate" is distinguished by manganese oxide and hydroxide dendrites and at least a hint of purple coloration. This material comes from privately held outcrops along the Quinn River in northwestern Nevada. In the specimen in the photograph, the dendrites are seen to radiate from cracks in the agate. The orangey yellow coloration in the lower part of the photograph may be assumed to come from disseminated goethite carried in solution that was impounded by the impermeable filling of the crack that rises from right to left in the photograph. The amethystine coloration in the upper portion of the specimen is supposed to have been caused by the replacement of some silicon ions in the agate's quartz lattice by ferric iron ions, with subsequent ejection under irradiation of unpaired oxygen electrons that then became trapped in atomic vacancies. These trapped electrons become "color centers" in the agate which, by absorbing yellow photons, make violet. The trade name of this agate variety seems to refer at once to two quite different plants: *sage* (brush), for its many-branched dendritic appearance, and *purple sage*, for its color. The bruised color of the corona around the dendrites where they ride through the purple sage might be termed "zane grey."

MOOKAITE *3x*
Mooka Station, Kennedy Range,
Carnarvon Shire, Gascoyne Region,
Western Australia, Australia

"Mookaite" is a specific trade name for a varicolored radiolarian chert (or jasper, by the definition that jasper is colored chert) that comes from a specific stratigraphic unit and locality in Western Australia. The stratigraphic unit is the Windalia Radiolarite, a sequence of radiolaria-rich sedimentary rocks laid down on a marine shelf 110 million years ago, during the Early Cretaceous epoch. Radiolaria are microscopic marine protozoans with skeletons made of opaline silica. Radiolarite is chert derived from radiolarian-rich mud by silica cementation and replacement. The source locality for "mookaite" is near Mooka Creek on Mooka Station—a 700,000-acre sheep ranch on the west side of the Kennedy Range, centered on the oasis of Mooka Spring. The ferromagnesian compounds that impart to mookaite all its colors are perhaps derived from the same mid-ocean-ridge basalt eruptions that pumped the excess silica into the ocean that fed the radiolarian bloom that ended up as radiolarite. *See also p. 125.*

CHRYSOCOLLA *2x*
Ray Mine, Hot Tamale Peak,
Mineral Creek District,
Pinal County, Arizona, USA

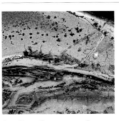

The rock called "chrysocolla" is a mélange of associated secondary copper minerals impregnated by varying amounts of silica. All of the colors in the specimen in the photograph are contributed by various compounds of copper that formed in the oxidation zone of the copper deposit that is exploited by the Ray Mine. The sky blue color overprinting the quartz veins in the lower half of the photograph is from the hydrous copper silicate, chrysocolla; the fringing darker blue is from the hydrous copper carbonate, azurite; the outermost green is from the hydrous copper carbonate, malachite; the black markings are the copper oxide, tenorite; the orangey-brown upper half of the photograph represents chalcedony colored by iron-bearing disseminations; quartz veins, some colored and some not, crisscross the specimen. *See also pp. 39, 43, and 145.*

IRON METEORITE *4x*
Near Tambo Quemado, Leoncio Prado District,
Lucanas Province, Ayacucho Department, Peru

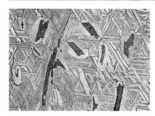

Among meteorites, iron octahedrite meteorites are the most prized as gemrock because their sawn and polished surfaces, when etched with nitric acid, typically display crisscross patterns called *Widmanstätten figures*, as in the photograph. Widmanstätten figures cannot be duplicated in the laboratory, because their formation requires cooling time (at a rate of less than 0.5 degree Celsius per 1,000 years) hundreds of times longer than human history. Individual meteorite specimens are designated by a concatenation of terms: locality/type, bandwidth/structural class, and chemical group. The full designation of the specimen in the photograph is *Tambo Quemado iron meteorite, medium octahedrite, Group IIIB*. Tambo Quemado is a village in a remote part of the high Andes near which a single 141-kilogram meteorite was discovered in 1950. An *iron meteorite* is a meteorite that is composed of iron-nickel metal in two distinct but intergrown alloy phases, both with the chemical formula of (Fe, Ni): *kamacite* (the broad beam-like lamellae in the photograph); and *taenite* (the more reflectant, thinner lamellae). An *octahedrite* is an iron meteorite in which the intergrowth of kamacite and taenite is structurally controlled by octahedral crystal geometry. *Medium octahedrite* is an octahedrite in which the kamacite lamellae are within the range of 0.5 to 1.3 millimeters. *Group IIIB* embraces meteorites from 233 meteorite fall localities around the world, including many of the largest irons ever found. All meteorites in Group IIIB are inferred to have formed in the differentiated molten core of an asteroid with an overall diameter of 17 miles and a core diameter of 7 miles. At some point in its post-fall history, the Tambo Quemado iron was artificially heated to 1000 degrees Celsius for an hour. This heating episode caused partial melting and recrystallization, evident in the blobbiness of the Widmanstätten figures. The Tambo Quemado iron contains many inclusions of cohenite (an iron carbide), which make cutting this meteorite difficult and expensive, since the diamond blades are quickly dulled and silicon carbide blades are required. Lapidaries must be careful when polishing any iron meteorite not to raise its temperature so much that the metal recrystallizes, as happened to the Tambo Quemado iron as the result of direct heating. *See also p. 73.*

PAGE 71
Tiger Iron *2x*
Ord Ranges, East Pilbara Shire,
Pilbara Region, Western Australia, Australia

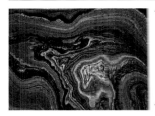

"Tiger iron" is a varietal trade name for a particular variety of metamorphic banded iron formation (BIF) rock called "jaspilite"—rock composed of highly folded, alternating bands of black and brown hematite and magnetite and red jasper—that is mined from the 3.2-billion-year-old Nimingarra Iron Formation on the northern edge of the Pilbara craton in Western Australia. BIFs are laterally extensive, marine-derived chemical sedimentary deposits consisting of alternating iron-rich (magnetite, siderite, or hematite) and iron-poor (dominantly silica) bands. Over 95 percent of the world's iron ore deposits are in BIFs. Over 90 percent of the world's BIFs were formed in the Early Proterozoic era between 2.5 and 2.0 billion years ago. In the specimen of BIF jaspilite in the photograph, the black bands are specular hematite; the red bands are red jasper; the yellow chatoyant areas are tiger's-eye jasper; and the white stringers in the black-and-white varved bands (alternating on the millimeter scale) are uncolored jasper. The Nimingarra BIFs are thought to have been laid down on a marine platform on the continental shelf of the Archean Pilbara craton. When iron-rich hydrothermal activity on the ocean floor was intense, hematite bands were precipitated; when hydrothermal activity was quiescent, silica bands were deposited; when there was intermittent upwelling (perhaps storm-induced) followed by cessation of upwelling from deeper ocean hematite-and-silica couplets were added to the varved bands. An essentially non-biogenic model is preferred because the stromatolites of the Warrawoona Formation, which is immediately below the Nimingarra Iron Formation, are scarcely 200 million years older than the Nimingarra BIFs. All the bands in the "tiger iron" in the photograph were originally horizontal. The flat bands were subsequently folded in a succession of metamorphic deformation events which also transformed ferromagnesian silicates in the jaspilite to riebeckite amphibole, then transformed the massive riebeckite to asbestiform crocidolite, and then transformed the blue crocidolite to yellow tiger's-eye.

PAGE 73
Iron Meteorite *3x*
Gibeon area, Namaland District,
Hardap Region, Namibia

A meteorite is a mass of solid matter that has fallen to the earth's surface from outer space. The full designation of the meteorite in the photograph is *Gibeon iron meteorite, fine octahedrite, Group IVA*. Gibeon is the nearest settlement to a meteorite field—discovered in 1836 and covering an arid tract 230 miles long by 70 miles wide in southern Namibia—whose surface was strewn with thousand of fragments of a parent meteorite that burst apart in the Earth's high atmosphere in recent prehistory. Thirty tons of irons have been surface-collected from the Gibeon meteorite field. An *iron meteorite* is a meteorite that is composed of iron-nickel metal in two distinct but intergrown alloy phases, both with the chemical formula of (Fe, Ni): *kamacite* (the broad beam-like lamellae in the photograph, with 4.5 to 13 percent nickel; from Greek for "lath"); and *taenite* (the more reflectant, thinner lamellae in the photograph, with more than 27 percent nickel; from Greek for "band"). The kamacite and taenite laths are contrasted in this specimen against a field of plessite (a fine-grained mixture of kamacite and taenite; from Greek for "filling"). An *octahedrite* is an iron meteorite in which the intergrowth of kamacite and taenite is structurally controlled by octahedral crystal geometry: two square-based pyramids joined congruently at their bases. The specimen in the photograph, showing Widmanstätten angles of 60 degrees, was cut parallel to a triangular face of the octahedral structure. *Fine octahedrite* is an octahedrite in which the kamacite lamellae are relatively thin: within the range of 0.2 to 0.5 millimeter in width (the specimen in the photograph has a kamacite bandwidth of 0.3 millimeter). *Group IVA* embraces meteorites from sixty-five meteorite fall localities around the world, all showing a unique trace element pattern marked by very low germanium (0.1 parts per million) and gallium (less than 2 ppm) values. All meteorites in Group IVA are inferred to have formed in the differentiated molten core of one small asteroid that was disrupted by a catastrophic impact shortly after its formation 4.6 billion years ago, and then by another impact 450 million years ago. *See also p. 69.*

PAGE 75
Pietersite *3x*
Farm Hopewell No. 204,
Outjo District, Kunene Region, Namibia

Pietersite—which is the informal gemrock name for the brecciated (mechanically ruptured, sheared, and contorted) form of tiger's-eye, which is in turn the pseudomorphous replacement of the asbestiform fibers of crocidolite by microcrystalline quartz—probably comes from only a single locality in the world: Farm Hopewell No. 204, one of 330 commercial farms in the Outjo District of northern Namibia. The pietersite collected from Farm Hopewell No. 204 occurs as allogenic detritus, in the form of cobbles stream-transported from an unknown source locality and scattered through the alluvial soil of the Ugab River valley. The deposit, discovered by the Namibian mineral dealer and prospector Sid Pieters in 1962, is reportedly now worked out. Sid Pieters (1920–2003) named his discovery *pietersite* after his father, Louis Pieters. In 1999, Sid Pieters himself was honored by having a new lead thiosulfate mineral from the Tsumeb mine formally named *sidpietersite* in recognition of his outstanding contributions to Namibian mineralogy. There is moreover a homophonic mineral, *petersite*—a radioactive hydrated phosphate from New Jersey formally named after Joe Peters (1951–) of the American Museum of Natural History. A second pietersite discovery, allegedly made in 1993 near Nanyang, Henan Province, was announced in China in 1997. Only small cut stones appeared on the market. When challenged to produce large roughs of their pietersite, the Chinese producers demurred, saying that their mine had flooded. Namibian producers charge that the alleged Chinese pietersite was in fact stolen from their cutting factories. Doubt has also been cast on claims that Chinese pietersite differs intrinsically from Namibian pietersite in being more golden in color and derived from a more magnesium-rich riebeckite. In the indubitably Namibian specimen in the photograph, the blue portion represents crocidolite ("blue asbestos") that has undergone little oxidation but severe mechanical disruption; whereas the red, orange, and yellow portion represents crocidolite that has undergone little mechanical disruption but extensive oxidation of the iron in the original composition, $Na_2(Fe,Mg)_3Fe_2Si_8O_{22}(OH)_2$.
See also pp. 21, 95, 105, 143, and 149.

MARRA MAMBA JASPER *2.5x*
Mount Brockman Station, Hamersley Range,
Ashburton Shire, Pilbara Region,
Western Australia, Australia

"Marra Mamba jasper" is a specific trade name for a gemrock from greenish and orangey brown jasper bands in a particular set of tiger's-eye-bearing banded iron formations (BIFs) in the Marra Mamba Iron Formation in the Hamersley iron ore province on the Pilbara craton of Western Australia. BIFs are laterally extensive, marine-derived chemical sedimentary deposits consisting of alternating iron-rich (magnetite, siderite, or hematite) and iron-poor (dominantly silica) bands. Over 95 percent of the world's iron ore deposits are in BIFs. Over 95 percent of Australia's iron ore resources are in the BIFs of the Late Archean to Early Proterozoic Hamersley Group in the Hamersley iron ore province, which is centered on the 4,000-foot-high Hamersley Range. The 750-foot-thick Marra Mamba Iron Formation, the lowermost unit of the one-and-a-half-mile-thick Hamersley Group, was deposited 3.63 billion years ago and outcrops today in the northern foothills of the Hamersley Range fronting the Fortescue River valley. It consists of BIFs interbedded with carbonates and shales. The Marra Mamba shales contain biological lipid microfossils whose analysis in 1997 showed that eukaryotes and cyanobacteria arose at least 500 million years before their fossil record begins and that photosynthesis evolved long before the atmosphere became oxidizing. Some BIFs of the Marra Mamba Iron Formation contain seams of crocidolite, some of which were converted to tiger's-eye by microcrystalline quartz replacement. "Marra Mamba jasper" is from jasper bands in Marra Mamba BIFs that contain tiger's-eye seams. The greenish jasper band in the specimen in the photograph is cut by a healed fracture rooted in a tiger's-eye seam, barely seen at the bottom of the photograph. The fracture and its ancillary cracks admitted iron-rich fluid into the jasper, where it precipitated red and yellow aureoles, within which millimeter-scale diffusion banding is evident in the photograph. *See also pp. 115 and 139.*

CRAZY LACE AGATE *3x*
Sierra Santa Lucia,
Chihuahua, Mexico

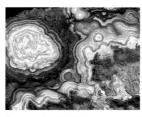

"Crazy lace agate" is a varietal trade name for an agate that is distinguished by multi-colored and twisting bands and that is mined from veins in limestone of the Sierra Santa Lucia in the Mexican states of Chihuahua and Durango. "Crazy lace agate" is significantly more permeable than Brazilian agate, allowing it to be dyed loud colors with aniline dyes. The specimen in the photograph, showing as it does numerous bands of pale gray and white, which are intrinsic pseudo-colors of unadulterated chalcedony, is all-natural in color. The reds, oranges, and yellows in the photograph of the specimen are all produced by iron oxide and hydroxide chromophores (chemical compounds producing color in the medium in which they occur), including hematite, hydrohematite, goethite, and hydrogeothite. These chromophores are enclosed in the chalcedonic micropores or finely dispersed. Beyond the basic color, the color tone of each colored band depends on the microstructure of the chalcedony in that band, in particular the quantity and size of the micropores. The high absorbent capacity of the micropores in "crazy lace agate" makes this variety of agate especially receptive to loud coloration by both natural and artificial agents. *See also pp. 31 and 89.*

SERAPHINITE *3x*
Korshunovskoye skarn-magnetite deposit,
east of Bratskoye Reservoir,
Angara-Ilim iron ore region, Irkutskaya Oblast,
Siberian Federal Okrug, Russia

"Seraphinite" is a trade name for a unique variety of clinochlore, which is a common phyllosilicate mineral species of the chlorite group with the chemical formula, $(Mg,Fe)_5Al(Si_3Al)O_{10}(OH)_8$. "Seraphinite" is distinguished exclusively by its habit: radiating bundles of silvery chatoyant fibers of clinochlore disposed within green masses of the same. "Seraphinite" comes only from one mine in the world: an iron ore deposit of the Angara-Ilim type located two hundred miles northwest of Lake Baikal. This skarn-magnetite deposit is in a breccia-fissure zone in the Paleozoic sedimentary cover on the Siberian Platform. "Seraphinite" shares with all clinochlore the properties of vitreous-to-pearly luster and softness (2 to 2.5 on the Mohs hardness scale). Its softness makes "seraphinite" easy to slab; but its fibrous habit makes it tricky to polish without undercutting.

OCEAN JASPER *1.5x*
Near Marovato, Ambolobozo District,
Mahajanga Province, Madagascar

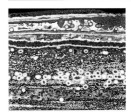

"Ocean jasper" is a trade name for a particular variety of orbicular jasper that is characterized by uniquely rich arrays of orbicules in a variety of colors, configurations, sizes, and morphologies. The specimen in the photograph shows a planar configuration presumably corresponding to the flow-banding planes of the original rhyolite, with each parallel plane containing orbicular aggregates of distinctive size, shape, color, and complexity. Because the original rhyolite has been converted to pure silica, "ocean jasper" readily conduces to being cut, polished, and worked into decorative shapes. This amenability to being worked, together with its extraordinary variety of color and pattern, makes "ocean jasper" an attractive material to lapidaries and jewelers. *See also pp. 15, 35, and 99.*

PAGE 85
GRAPHIC GRANITE *1.5x*
Madagascar

Graphic granite is a textural variety of granite (any coarse-grained igneous rock composed essentially of alkali feldspar and quartz) that is characterized by cuneiform figures of dark quartz arrayed with preferred orientations in a light-colored microcline matrix. Graphic ("writing") texture is caused by the ordered and intimate intergrowth of large crystals of quartz and microcline (potassium feldspar, $KAlSi_3O_8$), crystallizing simultaneously as the first-formed wall minerals from a body of granite magma that has a eutectic composition with respect to quartz and microcline (such that the two minerals are in equilibrium) and that is rich in volatiles such as water, fluorine, chlorine, or boron. Such volatiles, even though they are not incorporated in graphic granite, act to decrease the viscosity of the magma, depress the temperature of crystallization, and enhance chemical diffusion in the melt. In a melt of eutectic microcline-quartz composition, therefore, volatiles have the catalytic effect of promoting the simultaneous rate of growth of both sets of crystals so that they organize themselves into fairly regularly spaced rods of quartz interlocking with prisms of microcline along microcline's characteristic crystal faces. All the crystals in a given specimen of graphic granite have the same orientation: perpendicular to the wall of the magma chamber. Chunky "cuneiform writing" is seen when the specimen is cut perpendicularly to the lengths of the quartz rods. Longer-stemmed "Hebrew writing" is seen when the specimen is cut obliquely to the lengths of the quartz rods.

PAGE 87
MALACHITE *4x*
L'Etoile du Congo Mine, near Lubumbashi,
Katanga Copper Belt, Katanga Province,
Democratic Republic of the Congo

Malachite is hydrous copper carbonate—$Cu_2(CO_3)(OH)_2$—named for its characteristic green color (from the Greek word for "mallow", a plant with dark-green, kidney-shaped leaves). Malachite is the most common secondary mineral found in the oxidation zones of copper deposits, produced by the reaction of sulfides with carbonate gangue (non-economic rock hosting a metallic ore deposit). The specimen in the photograph, from the southern sector of the Katanga Copper Belt, is botryoidal (consisting of an aggregate of radiate bulbs resembling a bunch of grapes) in habit and shows characteristic concentric banding of diverse hues of green, ranging from very pale green through bright green to very dark green. Such bands are liable to have hardnesses so different from one another as to preclude cutting and polishing unless the whole specimen is impregnated with a resin. As a carbonate, malachite is not only relatively soft but also susceptible to acid attack. These frailties are overcome by a Russian simulant that appeared in 1988, all but indistinguishable from natural malachite except by destructive tests.

PAGE 89
AGUA NUEVA AGATE *1.5x*
Mi Sueno Claim, Rancho Agua Nueva,
Cerro de Aguja, Sierra del Gallego,
Chihuahua, Mexico

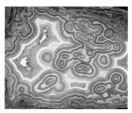

"Agua Nueva Agate" is a varietal trade name for an agate that is distinguished by multicolored and twisting bands and that is mined on the northern flank of Cerro de Aguja in the Sierra del Gallego from nodules and veins in andesites that erupted as flows and tuffs about 40 million years ago. It is named after Rancho Agua Nueva, where it was first mined. Agate in the outcrops and colluvium of the ranching area around Rancho Agua Nueva has been largely exhausted by surface collecting. Since ranchers do not countenance the digging of holes where their cattle graze, "Agua Nueva agates" have become increasingly scarce and expensive. "Agua Nueva agates" come in an array of colors, including pink, blue, and green. The specimen in the photograph is unusual for its bold amethystine hues, quite rare in agate. The amethystine color is supposed to have been caused by the replacement of some silicon ions in the agate's quartz lattice by ferric iron ions, with subsequent ejection under irradiation of unpaired oxygen electrons that then became trapped in atomic vacancies. These trapped electrons act as "color centers" in the agate by absorbing yellow photons to make violet. *See also pp. 31 and 79.*

PAGE 91
MOSS AGATE *3x*
Horse Canyon, Piute Mountains,
northeast of Tehachapi,
Kern County, California, USA

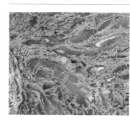

"Moss agate" is an informal variety of agate (translucent chalcedony or cryptocrystalline quartz) that is not banded but is instead variously splotched, commonly with arborescent shapes. In the specimen in the photograph, tendrils of unidentified iron silicate minerals are encapsulated in colorless agate. The agate veins of Horse Canyon in California's Piute Mountains cut through andesite of the Quaternary Tank Formation. Cracks forming in the cooling volcanic rock about one million years ago became filled with silica hydrogel, in which grains of iron-bearing minerals were suspended. These grains ruptured under osmotic pressure and shot out interbranching crystal tendrils. Horse Canyon, named for the fossil horses discovered there in 1916, has been closed to the public since 2000.

PAGE 93
SEPTARIUM *2.5x*
Long Valley near Orderville,
Kane County, Utah, USA

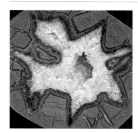

A septarium, also known as *septarian nodule*, is a carbonate concretion containing radial and concentric veins, called *septa* (from Latin for "partition"), that fill or partially fill crack voids with relatively coarse-grained carbonate minerals. A carbonate concretion, whether or not a septarium, is a hard, oblate ellipsoidal mass of impure calcareous argillite (a rock composed of clay-sized particles and intermediate in hardness between mudstone and shale) that differs in composition and texture from its host marine mudrocks. Carbonate concretions formed during sedimentation or diagenesis of their host mudrocks around nuclei of buried organic material, which released bacterial decomposition gases that set up local chemical conditions favorable to the deposition of the carbonate matrices of concretions. In septarian concretions, open fractures resulting from tensional failure and shrinkage became infilled with coarse-grained carbonate minerals precipitated on the fracture walls out of the pore-fluid in the cavities. The specimen in the photograph was dug out of the Tropic Shale, a 2,000-foot thickness of black carbonate mud laid down 90 million years ago in the Cretaceous Interior Seaway, which stretched from the Gulf of Mexico to Canada. The Tropic Shale sea bottom was an anoxic environment comparable to that of the modern Black Sea or Santa Barbara Basin off California. The fracture walls of the specimen in the photograph are lined with red-orange aragonite; the yellowish rhombohedral crystals infilling the void are the "dog-tooth spar" form of calcite. Aragonite and calcite are polymorphs of calcium carbonate ($CaCO_3$)—which is also the essential composition of the blackish matrix of the concretion.

PAGE 95
PIETERSITE *5x*
From Hopewell No. 204,
Outjo District, Kunene Region, Namibia

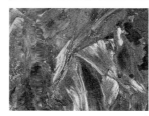

Pietersite—which is the informal gemrock name for the brecciated form of tiger's-eye—retains the parallel fibrous habit of its parent tiger's-eye. The fibrous parallelism in tiger's-eye is fairly uniform throughout the whole seam. In contrast, the fibrous parallelism in pietersite, which is derived from tiger's-eye by brecciation of the tiger's-eye seam, is fragmented into a mosaic of tesserae, in each of which the orientation of the fibrous parallelism is at odds with its neighbors. In hand specimen, pietersite retains the chatoyancy—the silky luster caused by the regular scattering of light among the closely packed parallel fibers of asbestiform silica—of the parent tiger's-eye. In pietersite, however, the chatoyancy is deranged into a dense mesh of chatoyant subdomains. *See also pp. 21, 75, 105, 143, and 149.*

PAGE 97
FLUORITE-OPAL NODULE *2.5x*
Brush Wellman Beryllium Mine, Spor Mountain,
Juab County, Utah, USA

Fluorite-opal nodules come from the upper part of the 21-million-year-old basal tuff (rock composed of volcanic fragments) of the Spor Mountain Formation, a sequence of rhyolites erupted from a belt of volcanic calderas in western Utah during the Miocene. The fluorite-opal nodules were originally carbonate clasts that had been ripped out of the dolomitic country rock and incorporated into the basal tuff during eruption. The carbonate clasts were then altered by fluorine-rich mineralizing fluids rising through faults and rhyolite vents into the basal tuff and reacting with the calcium in the carbonate clasts to precipitate fluorite, beryllium (in the form of submicroscopic bertrandite inclusions in the fluorite), and uranium (dispersed in the lattice of the fluorite). The alteration sequence of the carbonate clasts is from dolomite to calcite to microcrystalline quartz to opal-fluorite. This sequence is centrifugally repeated in individual nodules, which commonly have a calcite core, a microcrystalline quartz middle zone, and an outer zone of intergrown fluorite and opal. The specimen in the photograph comes from the outer fluorite-opal zone, which contains the economically valuable beryllium and uranium. The purple coloration in the specimen comes from the fluorite. Where the purple is faded or absent, opal predominates. The crack in middle of the yellowish region in the upper right of the photograph is a shrinkage void caused by opal dehydration. The fluorite-opal nodules of the basal tuff of the Spor Mountain Formation are the United States' main source of beryllium, a poisonous light metal with many industrial applications. Not more than one percent of the fluorite-opal zone in the nodules is bertrandite.

PAGE 99
OCEAN JASPER *1.5x*
Near Marovato, Ambolobozo District,
Mahajanga Province, Madagascar

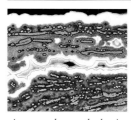

"Ocean jasper" is a trade name for a particular variety of orbicular jasper that is characterized by uniquely rich arrays of orbicules in a variety of colors, configurations, sizes, and morphologies. The specimen in the photograph shows a planar configuration presumably corresponding to the flow-banding planes of the original rhyolite, with subparallel planes alternating between segmented single-layer chains of small, weakly differentiated orbicules; spheroids consisting of nuclei encased in drusy green coronas; and white microcrystalline quartz, with one such planar layer enclosing an elongated miarolotic cavity lined with euhedral druse. "Ocean jasper" has been available commercially since the 2000 Tucson Gem and Mineral Show, where it appeared as a result of the discovery two years before of the source bed in the intertidal zone of a remote section of the northwestern coast of Madagascar. A few specimens had been acquired by collectors on the open market in preceding decades and conveyed to European museums, beginning in 1927 with the acquisition by the Museum of Mineralogy and Geology in Dresden of the 9,000-piece collection of Richard Baldauf, which contained an "ocean jasper" under the name of *Augenjaspis* (eye jasper). The exact provenance within Madagascar of these museum specimens remained unknown, however, until Paul Obenich's find in 1998. *See also pp. 15, 35, and 83.*

Owyhee Picture Jasper 2x
*Owyhee Uplands between Owyhee Reservoir
and Three Fingers Rock,
Malheur County, Oregon, USA*

"Owyhee picture jasper" is a specific trade name for a silicified rhyolitic tuff with distinctive ochre and yellow patterns or a pale blue ground and that is mined from a locality six miles west of Succor Creek State Park in the Owyhee Uplands of Oregon. The "Owyhee picture jasper" ashfall tuff was erupted 11 million years ago from a rhyolitic volcanic center in the Basin and Range province to the south. This rhyolite unit is sandwiched between basalts extruded from the Snake River Plain to the north. Transition metal ions from the basalts were mobilized by hydrothermal solutions and precipitated along cracks in the tuff as ochre hydrohematite, yellow goethite, and manganese dendrites. The "Owyhee picture jasper" tuff has been sufficiently impregnated and indurated by silica to take a good polish *See also p. 41.*

Munjina Stone 5x
*Chichester Range, East Pilbara Shire,
Pilbara Region, Western Australia, Australia*

"Munjina stone" is a specific trade name for a silicified shale with colorful patterns from the Chichester Range in Western Australia. The silicified shale comes from a transition zone in the Late Archean to Early Proterozoic Hamersley Group. This transition zone straddles the top of the Mount McRae Shale and the bottom of the Dales Gorge Member of the Brockman Iron Formation, both units consisting of massive fine-grained shales interbedded with cherts and banded iron formations (BIFs), laid down on the continental shelf of the Pilbara craton 2.47 billion years ago. Some of the shale beds in this zone were later invaded along fractures by solutions heated and enriched by metamorphic chemical reactions in the BIFs. Silica and iron ions from the BIFs that were mobilized in the heated solutions were then precipitated in the porous shale as white silica, red hematite and yellow goethite, in conformably banded tongues narrowing toward the crack tips.

Pietersite 3x
*Farm Hopewell No. 204,
Outjo District, Kunene Region, Namibia*

Pietersite—the brecciated form of tiger's-eye, which is in turn the pseudomorphous replacement of the asbestiform fibers of crocidolite by microcrystalline quartz—generally retains to a greater or lesser extent patches of the blue color of its grandparent crocidolite ("blue asbestos"), which was in turn derived from massive riebeckite ("blue amphibole"). In other patches of most pietersite specimens, the blue color is altered to a rich array of shades of red, orange, yellow, and green. Depending on the specimen in question, this complex alteration might have occurred as a result of a number of different processes, working together or independently. Stress-induced disruption of coordination polyhedra in the crystal structure of crocidolite could have facilitated the liberation of iron ions from the crocidolite—$Na_2(Fe,Mg)_3Fe_2Si_8O_{22}(OH)_2$—to be expressed as inherent red chromophores. Redox and water fugacity conditions attending the silica replacement of the crocidolite could have permitted the ferric and ferrous iron to bond with oxygen and water to produce disseminated hematite (red) and goethite (yellow) in locally varying proportions. Bonding of iron ions with the sodium ions liberated from the crocidolite crystal structure could have produced the green color characteristic of ferrous salts. Charge transfer transitions between adjacent ferric and ferrous ions could have produced characteristic colors at the warm end of the spectrum. The permeation of pietersite by silica is made evident in the specimen in the photograph by the banded agate inclusion that fills the cavity in the lower left-hand corner. *See also pp. 21, 75, 95, 143, and 149.*

Black Opal 9x
*Mulga Field, Lightning Ridge,
Walgett Shire, New South Wales, Australia*

"Black opal" is a trade name for a variety of opal that is mined in only three localities, all of them in Australia. The most notable source of black opals is the opal field near the town of Lightning Ridge in northern New South Wales. Black opal is characterized by brilliant "play of color" (hence a "precious opal") over a background ("body color") of black or dark gray "potch" (opal lacking "play of color"). Black opal is the most brilliantly colorful and most valuable opal variety in the world, typically commanding hundreds of dollars per carat. In precious opal, the close-packed, uniformly sized silica spheres form regular planes that diffract visible light. The diffracted wavelength is similar in magnitude to the distance between the planes of spheres: on the order of several hundreds of nanometers (10^{-7} meter). Silica spheres with diameters greater than 138 nanometers diffract light into wavelengths greater than 380 nanometers, corresponding to violet and blue colors. Spheres with diameters greater than 241 nanometers diffract light into wavelengths greater than 647 nanometers, corresponding to red—as well as into the shorter wavelengths of all the other colors. As a result, rare black opals with red fire—such as the specimen in the photograph—show the whole spectrum. In precious opals, the shapes of domains of differently sized spheres determine the patterns of the play of color. Black opal that shows broad patterns—as in the specimen in the photograph, which has a "straw pattern"—is more rare and costly than black opal with narrow "pinfire patterns." All New South Wales opals, including the specimen in the photograph, are mined from the Early Cretaceous Roma Formation, composed of mudstones and clayey sandstone laid down 115 million years ago. Opal is preferentially concentrated along one particular mudstone bed, occurring in flattened nodules called "nobbies." On account of their high water content (10 weight percent), Lightning Ridge opals are liable to crazing (spontaneous cracking from dehydration of the silica gel in the void space of the packed silica spheres) and are put into humidified storage immediately upon extraction from the earth. *See also pp. 25, 113, 121, and 151.*

PAGE 109
RHODONITE *3x*
Tamworth, New South Wales, Australia

Rhodonite is essentially manganese silicate—$MnSiO_3$—with variable substitution of manganese by calcium, iron. and magnesium. Like rhodochrosite, rhodonite is named from the Greek word for "rose." Like its linguistic cognate, rhodonite's distinctive pink color comes from its divalent manganese ions. Unlike its carbonate cousin, however, rhodonite is a hard silicate mineral that is resistant to acid attack. The specimen in the photograph was mined twenty miles north of the town of Tamworth, where the Late Devonian Tamworth belt of the New England Orogen is exposed in northern New South Wales. The product of contact metamorphism of impure limestones 370 million years ago, the specimen in the photograph is massive and compact in habit, with a vitreous luster. The variegated mottles are phantom relics of portions of the calcic wall rock. The pink color in the specimen in the photograph varies in brightness according to local calcium content: from bright pink for low calcium to pale pink for high calcium. The brown patch in the middle of the photograph indicates higher iron content. The spidery black lines in the specimen are manganese oxides and hydroxides that precipitated from fluid solutions that entered into cracks. The wife of Tsar Alexander II, Maria Alexandrovna, who died of languishing tuberculosis in 1880, is entombed beside her husband in the Cathedral of Sts. Peter and Paul in St. Petersburg in a 12-ton sarcophagus carved at the Peterhof Lapidary Works from a 45-ton rhodonite monolith quarried from the Maloe Sedelnikovskoye deposit in the Ural Mountains. The nearby Church of the Savior-on-the-Blood (Khram Spasas na Krovi) was built over the spot on the Catherine Canal Embankment on which Alexander II (after whom the dark green variety of chrysoberyl *alexandrite* was named) was assassinated by a bomb-thrower in 1881. The precise spot on the pavement on which the bleeding body of the tsar fell in the snow is preserved and covered with a stone canopy festooned with bright pink flowers carved from the same rhodonite from which his wife's sarcophagus is made.

PAGE 111
CHAROITE *3x*
Sirenevoy Kamen Deposit, Maly Murun Massif, Olekmo-Charskoye Upland, Sakha Republic, Russia

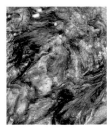

The mineral charoite is a hydrated inosilicate of lilac color with the chemical composition, $(K,Na)_5(Ca,Ba,Sr)_8(Si_6O_{15})_2(Si_2O_7)Si_4C_9(OH,F)\cdot3(H_2O)$ The lilac color grades to violet and lavender with a range of pink, bluish, reddish, and brown hues It weathers to white. Just as the pink coloration of rhodonite and rhodochrosite is attributed to the presence of manganese in its divalent ionic form, so the lilac coloration of charoite is attributed to presence of manganese in its trivalent ionic form, where it substitutes for silicon in the crystal structure. The specimen in the photograph represents a morphological variety of charoite aggregate called "scaly" or "glimmeritic", in which microblocks of charoite with parallel-fibrous structure grow together at various angles. Charoite comes from a single deposit in southwestern Sakha Republic (formerly Yakutia), very near the border with Irkutskaya Oblast. *See also pp. 49 and 141.*

PAGE 113
MATRIX OPAL *7x*
Koroit Opal Field, Paroo Shire, Warrego District, Queensland, Australia

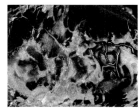

"Matrix opal" is opal that infills intergranular pores, cracks, and voids in siliceous ironstone concretions ("boulders") found in Queensland. The "matrix opal" in a given boulder might be "precious" (showing "play of color") or "common" (lacking "play of color")—or both (in which case the common opal is called "potch"). In the specimen in the photograph, the blue sparkly material is precious opal, the creamy orange material is potch, and the black matrix is ironstone. The hotchpotch of precious opal and potch in the photograph infills cracks and voids in the outer part of the ellipsoidal boulder. Opal is an amorphous or cryptocrystalline aggregate of hydrous silica—$SiO_2\cdot n(H_2O)$—containing from 1 to 21 weight percent water. It is the lowest temperature modification of silica. In the environment of a chemically weathered soil profile, opal is precipitated from remobilized silica at 70 to 120 degrees Fahrenheit. Opal grows by very slow crystallization (on the order of an inch in ten million years) of submicroscopic spheres (on the order of 10^{-7} meter in diameter) out of interstitial silica gel. In eastern Australia, all opal deposits occur in the profile of chemical weathering (15 to 150 feet thick) that formed during the Miocene in the top of the near-shore marine and continental sandstone and clay beds of Cretaceous age in the Great Artesian Basin. All Queensland boulder opals, including the specimen in the photograph, occur in the Winton Formation, composed of sandstones, siltstones, mudstones, and claystones laid down 95 million years ago. The opal-bearing belt of weathered Winton Formation is 200 miles wide by 600 miles long, stretching across western Queensland northward from the border with New South Wales. In the Winton Formation weathered profile, opal accumulated predominantly in the lowermost kaolinized (bleached) zone. In the Koroit field, the opal occurs at the bottom of a sandstone bed, in a densely ferruginous (iron-bearing) horizon, 1 to 10 feet thick. Precious opal constitutes less than five percent of the opal present. *See also pp. 25, 107, 121, and 151.*

PAGE 115

MARRA MAMBA TIGER'S-EYE *2x*
Mount Brockman Station, Hamersley Range,
Ashburton Shire, Pilbara Region,
Western Australia, Australia

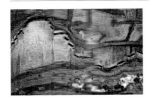

"Marra Mamba tiger's-eye" is a specific trade name for tiger's-eye that comes from certain banded iron formations (BIFs) in the Marra Mamba Iron Formation in the Hamersley iron ore province of Western Australia. BIFs are laterally extensive marine-derived chemical sedimentary deposits consisting of alternating iron-rich and iron-poor bands. Over 95 percent of Australia's iron ore resources are in BIFs of the Late Archean to Early Proterozoic Hamersley Group. The basal unit of the one-and-a-half-mile-thick Hamersley Group is the Marra Mamba Iron Formation, chemically precipitated in a marine basin 3.63 billion years ago. Some BIFs of the Marra Mamba Iron Formation contains seams of crocidolite, some of which have been converted to tiger's-eye by microcrystalline quartz replacement. "Marra Mamba tiger's-eye" is mined from outcrops of the Marra Mamba Iron Formation in the northern foothills of the Hamersley Range fronting the Fortescue River valley, thirty miles west of Karijini National Park. The tiger's-eye started as massive riebeckite ("blue amphibole")—$Na_2(Fe,Mg)_3Fe_2Si_8O_{22}(OH)_2$—which was then transformed under shearing stress to its asbestiform allomorph, crocidolite ("blue asbestos"). The crocidolite then underwent transformation to hawk's-eye (still blue), as the closely packed, micron-scale, parallel crocidolite fibers were permeated and partially replaced by microcrystalline quartz. The transformation of hawk's-eye (blue) to tiger's-eye (golden yellow and reddish brown) occurred by the alteration of crocidolite fibers to hydrous iron oxide together with further replacement of the hawk's-eye by microcrystalline quartz pseudomorphs. The greenish cast of the tiger's-eye in the specimen in the photograph results from incomplete transformation of the precursory hawk's-eye (blue) to tiger's-eye (yellow). The track of opaque magnetite bodies in the tiger's-eye seam appears to represent the selvage of a reduction front that was subsequently segmented mechanically, perhaps by the tensional forces responsible for the boudinage (pinch-and-swell structure) of the tiger's-eye seam. The "Marra Mamba jasper" enclosing the tiger's-eye seam in the specimen in the photograph is colored orangey brown from iron oxides and hydroxides. *See also pp. 77 and 139.*

PAGE 117

PETRIFIED WOOD *4x*
Near Petrified Forest National Park,
Apache County, Arizona, USA

Petrified wood is a variety of jasper formed by permineralization or replacement of wood tissue by silica precipitated from silica-rich aqueous solution. The silica-saturated groundwater that petrified the buried tree trunks of Apache County's Petrified Forest generally contained various metal oxides and ions that imparted their characteristic colors to the transparent-to-translucent base complexion of the quartz ground. Where such chromogenic agents were lacking, as in the fully replaced specimen in the photograph, the silica shows its intrinsic milky-bluish complexion. All the petrified wood exposed in the national park and its environs comes from several beds in the Chinle Formation, laid down in the age of the early dinosaurs. The Chinle Formation is a continental sequence of conglomerate, sandstone, and mudstone deposited by meandering rivers in a back-arc basin on the western margin of the Pangaean supercontinent between 220 and 210 million years ago. During this Late Triassic deposition, the Chinle basin was situated in the tropical belt at about ten degrees north paleolatitude, corresponding to the present latitude of the northern Congo basin. The depositional environment of the Chinle basin—including channels, overbank and crevasse splays, and floodplains—was rather like that of the comparably sized and situated modern Congo basin. As in the modern Congo basin, siliciclastic sediment was shed from mountain belts bordering the Chinle basin onto a floodplain covered by equatorial forest supported by a tropical wet climate. The beds exposed in Petrified Forest National Park that contain petrified wood were deposited by floods. *See also pp. 13, 17, 135, and 137.*

PAGE 119

BANDED AGATE *4x*
Rio Grande do Sul, Brazil

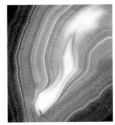

Banded agate is an agate (a translucent chalcedony or cryptocrystalline quartz) that is distinguished by either concentric banding or plane banding. Banded agate from Rio Grande do Sul is of the concentric variety on account of its mode of formation: in amygdules within basaltic lava flows of the 130-million-year-old Serra Geral Formation. The amygdules were initially filled with hydrosol (a colloidal system in which water is the dispersion medium for silica polymers) under high internal pressure. The hydrosol then dehydrated into silica gel, which in turn crystallized and coated the walls of the amygdule concentrically and centripetally, imitating the shape of the original cavity. The banding of the specimen in the photograph is grayish-brown, bluish gray, pale gray, grayish white, and milky white—with an overall tendency to progress from dark on the outside to light at the center. The gray and white hues are all intrinsic pseudo-colors of chalcedony that depend not on compositional differences but on the diffusive effects of variations in the quantity and size of micropores in and among the microfibers making up the chalcedony of each agate band. The grayish-brown outer bands owe their coloration to chromophores enclosed in the chalcedonic micropores or finely dispersed as oxides and hydroxides of iron. *See also pp. 33 and 153.*

KOROIT NUT OPAL *3x*
Koroit Opal Field, Paroo Shire,
Warrego District, Queensland, Australia

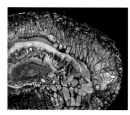

"Koroit nut opal" is a specific variety of "boulder opal" (any opal that infills cracks, pores and voids in certain siliceous ironstone concretions that are found in a particular region of Queensland and are called "boulders"), in which the boulder is of a specific size range ("nut" size), morphology (concentric radial infilling), and source locality (the Koroit opal field). "Koroit nut opal" is similar to the more famous "Yowah nut opal," which is mined eighty miles to the southwest of Koroit from the same chemically weathered profile within the Late Cretaceous Winton Formation, which covers an vast tract of western Queensland. Both the "Koroit" and "Yowah nuts" are siliceous ironstone concretions that are ellipsoidal in shape, range in size from a pea to a football (the "Koroit nut" in the photograph being 5 inches across), and host a network of opal veinlets in concentric and radial fissures. Both "Koroit" and "Yowah nuts" occur in distinct nut horizons, 6 to 20 inches wide, in kaolinized (bleached) sandstone near the bottom of the weathered profile. Only a small proportion of nuts contain precious opal. In the specimen in the photograph, the red ironstone core is successively nested in: a shell of largely intact buff-colored ferruginous (iron-bearing) sandstone, a shell of blue and purple opal, a shell of largely intact ferruginous sandstone, a shell of ferruginous sandstone cut by radial fissures filled with blue and purple opal, and an ironstone casing filled with tangles of black iron oxide admixed with blebs of opal. From the violet and blue colors of the opal, it may be inferred that the constituent silica spheres in the opal are in the range of 140 to 200 nanometers in diameter. *See also pp. 25, 107, 113, and 151.*

PAESINA MARBLE *1.5x*
Tuscany, Italy

"Paesina marble" is an adaptation of the Italian term *pietra paesina*—meaning "landscape stone." *Pietra paesina* is a variety of the slightly clayey carbonate siltstones of Tuscany's Alberese facies, laid down at the dawn of the Paleocene epoch, 64 million years ago. Not having undergone metamorphic recrystallization, *pietra paesina* is strictly not a marble but a limestone. The polyhedral texture of *pietra paesina* results from the development under regional stress of pervasive joint sets, subsequently cemented by impermeable calcite in the fractures bounding the polygonal compartments. Liesegang bands formed when oxygen in ground water diffused into the compartments, which contained soluble ferrous iron in the pore water of the carbonate siltstone. Each calcite-sealed polygonal compartment behaved as an independent diffusion cell—hence the quite independent colors and patterns engendered by the iron oxide in each compartment. Filippo Napoletano (*c.* 1587–1629), painter of imaginary landscapes for the Medicis, specialized in painting directly on polished slabs of *pietra paesina*, placing his human figures from Dante and Ariosto amid the "deserts" and "burning cities" of the natural stone. Painted *pietra paesina* is sometimes called "ruin stone." In the posthumously published catalogue of his celebrated cabinet of natural wonders in Copenhagen, the Museum Wormianum, Olaus Worm (1588–1654) wrote of his specimen of *pietra paesina* that it showed "in one part towers, in other parts buildings, mountains, rivers, and complete cities … Nature has joked uncommonly in the outward appearances of natural things."

MOOKAITE *3x*
Mooka Station, Kennedy Range,
Carnarvon Shire, Gascoyne Region,
Western Australia, Australia

"Mookaite" is a specific trade name for a varicolored radiolarian chert that comes from the 110-million-year-old Windalia Radiolarite in the Carnarvon Basin of Western Australia. Radiolarite is inherently colorless, being a massive form of cryptocrystalline quartz that developed from siliceous ooze on the sea bottom comprised in large measure of the opaline skeletons of radiolaria, single-celled zooplankton that can flourish in silica-saturated seas. The ferromagnesian compounds that impart to mookaite its many colors are perhaps derived from the same submarine basalt eruptions that saturated the Early Cretaceous sea on the Carnarvon platform with silica, enabling the Windalia radiolarian population to burgeon. The solutions that imported the iron and magnesium chromophores (disseminated color agents) into the "mookaite" were delivered and distributed by generations of cracks, whose geometry dictated the geometry of the color bands in the porous stone, such that a color-specific solution might be admitted along one open crack while being at the same time confined by the edge of another impermeable crack. The color halos in the specimen in the photograph narrow toward the crack tips. *See also p. 65.*

PAGE 127
RHODOCHROSITE *3x*
Capillitas Mine, Andalgalá Department,
Catamarca Province, Argentina

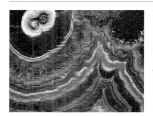

Rhodochrosite is manganese carbonate ($MnCO_3$). It belongs to the calcite mineral group and—like calcite (calcium carbonate, $CaCO_3$)—occurs in nature both as rhombohedral crystals and as radiate banded concretionary aggregates, including stalactites (as is the specimen in the photograph). Thanks in part to pointing by manganese pink (the word *rhodochrosite* is derived from Greek for "rose-colored") banding in rhodochrosite stalactites is more conspicuous than in the carbonate, phosphate, or sulfate stalactites that grow in karst caverns. The locality from which the specimen in the photograph comes—the Capillitas mine at over ten thousand feet in the Andes of northwestern Argentina—is the source of virtually all the rhodochrosite stalactites on the world market. The Capillitas mine—first opened for silver extraction by the Incas whose empire expanded to include the area of Catamarca during the second half of the fifteenth century—was intensively developed by the Argentine military during World War II for its strategic copper content. The Capillitas mining operations exploit a number of major veins, totaling fifteen miles in length and averaging several feet in lenticular thickness, resulting from epithermal (near-surface hydrothermal) silver-copper-zinc-lead-manganese mineralization of two sets of faults and fractures associated with a volcanic chimney that erupted pyroclastics and lava onto Paleozoic granite five million years ago. The Capillitas deposits are the most diverse in Argentina, yielding 83 mineral species. One of the Capillitas veins—the 25 de Mayo—is characterized by abundant cavities housing rhodochrosite stalactites, which commonly exceed six inches in diameter and three feet in length. The stalactite in the photograph, which is revealed in basal section to have grown from twinned growth centers, has a diameter of almost five inches. Although rhodochrosite stalactites are morphologically similar to speleothems (banded cave deposits, including carbonate, phosphate, and sulfate stalactites), they form in a hydrothermal environment 150 to 200 degrees Celsius hotter than a karst cave environment; require two orders of magnitude longer time to form—as long as half-a-million years; and display more complex banding patterns in result of higher chemical activity at higher temperatures.

PAGE 129
HICKORYITE *4x*
Rodeo area, Durango, Mexico

"Hickoryite" is a varietal trade name for silicified banded rhyolite from the area of Rodeo in the state of Durango. Rhyolite is a volcanic rock with the composition of granite but its quickly cooled crystals are too small to be seen with the unaided eye. "Hickoryite" was erupted as volcanic ash and underwent hydrothermal silicification after deposition. The red (hematitic) banding is a Liesegang phenomenon, meaning that reactants in a gel diffuse and precipitate in relation to a moving reaction boundary in an ordered way such that the concentrations of the reactants dynamically organize themselves into parallel bands within the gel. The identification of the specimen's banding as a Leisegang phenomenon is consistent with the style of deformation in the banding caused by the dilatant crack traveling from the right of the photograph. The dimpling of the banding without rupture implies that the originally concentric banding was organized while the silicified rhyolite was in a gel state and before the crack formed. It implies conversely that the crack formed while the silicified rhyolite was still somewhat plastic, prior to its complete crystallization into "hickoryite."

PAGE 131
MORRISONITE *2.5x*
Morrison Ranch, Owyhee River Canyon,
Malheur County, Oregon, USA

"Morrisonite" is a specific trade name for a varicolored jasper mined from a brecciated outcrop on the cliffs of the Owyhee River Canyon. Pervasive cracks in the specimen in the photograph have been sealed with colored chalcedony, dividing the "morrisonite" into polygonal compartments. Liesegang phenomena occurred when iron-bearing hydrothermal fluids diffused into the compartments. Each silica-sealed polygonal compartment behaved as an independent diffusion cell—hence the largely independent colors, shades, and patterns engendered by the iron oxide budgets in each compartment. "Morrisonite" is named after Jim Morrison, a bachelor from West Virginia who started up the Morrison Ranch about 1900 and lived in a rock cabin at the bottom of the Owyhee River canyon for the next sixty years. He is not buried in the Père-Lachaise Cemetery. He is credited with finding the first piece of "morrisonite" in his irrigation ditch and tracing it back to its source up in the volcanic cliffs. "Morrisonite" was first advertised in rockhound magazines in 1947. The Morrison Ranch was acquired by the Bureau of Land Management in 1988 as part of its program to protect the wild and scenic values of the thousand-foot-deep Owyhee River canyon. *See also p. 45.*

PAGE 133
PETRIFIED WOOD *3x*
Devils Gate, Hubbard Basin,
Elko County, Nevada, USA

Petrified wood is a variety of jasper formed by permineralization or replacement of wood tissue by silica precipitated from silica-rich aqueous solution. The petrified tree trunk of the specimen in the photograph was buried in the volcanic ash of the Jarbridge Rhyolite bed, laid down in Hubbard Basin in northeastern Nevada 11 million years ago at the end of the Middle Miocene by the eruption of the Bruneau-Jarbridge supervolcano, eighty miles to the north in southwestern Idaho. The silica-saturated groundwater that petrified the tree trunks buried in the silica-rich Jarbridge Rhyolite bed also transported into the wood the iron oxides that imbue the specimen in the photograph with its reddish-brown colors. Several later cracks (horizontal in the photograph) are the axial loci of local overprinting by deep red hematite. Blebs of colorless silica can be seen in the crack running vertically across the left half of the photograph.

PAGE 135
PETRIFIED WOOD *2.5x*
Near Petrified Forest National Park,
Apache County, Arizona, USA

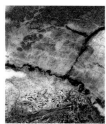

Petrified wood is a variety of jasper formed by permineralization or replacement of wood tissue by silica precipitated from silica-rich aqueous solution. All the petrified wood exposed in Petrified Forest National Park and its environs comes from the Chinle Formation, laid down in the age of the early dinosaurs. Exposures of Chinle rocks occur widely on the Colorado Plateau, covering extensive portions of Arizona, New Mexico, Colorado, Utah, Idaho, and Wyoming. Outcrops of the Chinle Formation within Petrified Forest National Park consist of multicolored mudstones, sandstone, conglomerate, and limestone beds, conventionally divided into five members having a cumulative thickness of a thousand feet. Petrified wood is found throughout the geographic range of the Chinle Formation—and indeed petrified wood is found in every state of the Union. The densest concentration of petrified wood in the world occurs in Petrified Forest National Park. In the park, the densest concentrations of petrified wood occur in two beds of one member of the Chinle Formation: the Sonsela Sandstone Bed and Black Forest Bed of the Petrified Forest Member. The largest concentrations of petrified wood in the park are called "forests" and given names that reflect some property of their wood. The Rainbow, Crystal, and Jasper Forests in the southern end of the park all derive from the Sonsela Sandstone bed. The Black Forest in the northern part of the park derives from the Black Forest bed, which, varying in thickness from zero to fifty feet, was deposited by a catastrophic flood. Ferric oxide (hematite) imbues the quartz with red; iron hydroxide (hydrogoethite), yellow and buff; chromium ions, green; cobalt ions, blue. Petrified logs that contain organic traces, not having undergone complete replacement, tend to have carbon-dark features, such as the specimen in the photograph. *See also pp. 13, 17, 117, and 137.*

PAGE 137
PETRIFIED WOOD *2x*
Near Petrified Forest National Park,
Apache County, Arizona, USA

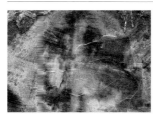

Ninety percent of the petrified wood in Petrified Forest National Park and its vicinity belongs to an extinct tree species named *Araucarioxylon arizonicum*, with the remainder belonging to two smaller species, *Woodworthia arizonica* and *Schilderia adamanica*. *Araucarioxylon arizonicum* was a tall single-trunked conifer with a maximum height of nearly 200 feet and a breast height diameter of ten feet. *Araucarioxylon* was quite unlike its modern namesake, the araucaria, in having a massive vertical taproot, branches that grew haphazardly on the trunk from its base to its crown, and no growth rings. Many fossilized trunks in Petrified Forest National Park show girdling by bark beetles. Some trunks contain the silicified remains of large nests identical in structure to bee hives, suggesting that bees predate the appearance of flowering plants by over a hundred million years. Ferric oxide (hematite) imbues the quartz with red; iron hydroxide (hydrogoethite), yellow and buff; chromium ions, green; cobalt ions, blue. Petrified logs that contain organic traces, not having undergone complete replacement, tend to have carbon-dark features, such as the specimen in the photograph. The Black Forest bed is named for the carbon-dark features in its petrified wood, which was buried by a catastrophic flood. The flood was induced by ash fall from volcanoes in eastern California and western Nevada, which choked and swelled the meandering channels of the floodplain. Lateral migration of the channel through the area of the Black Forest undercut living trees on the outside of meanders and buried them in ashy point bars on the inside of meanders. Overbanking and rupture of the channel banks resulted in avulsion, or catastrophic change of course of the river out onto the floodplain. Avulsion uprooted the trees growing on the banks and buried them in the splay deposits, which were then capped by tuffaceous (ash-bearing) sandstone deposited by the new river channel. The permineralized logs of the Black Forest bed are preserved at the base of the overlying tuffaceous sandstone. *See also pp. 13, 17, 117, and 135.*

PAGE 139
MARRA MAMBA TIGER'S-EYE *2x*
Mount Brockman Station, Hamersley Range,
Ashburton Shire, Pilbara Region,
Western Australia, Australia

"Marra Mamba tiger's-eye" is a specific trade name for tiger's-eye that comes from certain banded iron formations (BIFs) in the Marra Mamba Iron Formation in the Hamersley Group of Western Australia. The top of the Marra Mamba Iron Formation contains a four-foot-thick bed rich in microtektites (silicate glass droplets resulting from extraterrestrial impacts) that was deposited by a tsunami created by an asteroid impact 3.63 billion years ago. The orangey reddish cast of the tiger's-eye in the specimen in the photograph is typical of "Marra Mamba tiger's-eye" and reveals the presence of the same assemblage of iron oxides and hydroxides that color the neighboring jasper band. Tiger-eye's chatoyancy—its silky luster caused by the regular scattering of light among the closely packed parallel fibers of asbestiform silica, best appreciated by rocking a properly cut and highly polished hand specimen gently under a point light source—is maximized by sawing the rough parallel to the lay of the asbestiform fibers, as was done in the specimen in the photograph. A practical difficulty in this lapidary operation is encountered where fibers deviate from perfect parallelism in the rock. *See also pp. 77 and 115.*

CHAROITE *2x*

Sirenevyi Kamen Deposit, Maly Murun Massif,
Olekmo-Charskoye Upland, Sakha Republic, Russia

The mineral charoite is a hydrated inosilicate of lilac color that is inferred to have a precise chemical composition and crystal structure. In the Sirenevyi Kamen deposit in Siberia, which is the only place in the world where the mineral is found, charoite never occurs in a pure crystalline form but is always intimately admixed with other minerals. The material marketed as "charoite" is in fact a charoititic rock whose true charoite content ranges between 30 and 95 percent. So inextricably intergrown is charoite with other minerals that charoite has never been successfully isolated in a monomineralic fraction for crystal-diffraction analysis. The specimen in the photograph represents a morphological variety of charoite aggregate called "radial fibrous", in which filamentary crystals ("whiskers") of charoite are disposed in radial clusters that display a silky chatoyancy. Many such whiskers in the photograph are pointed by weathering to white and by intergrowth with orangey-brown tinaksite. The interstitial black masses among the charoite radial clusters are aegerine. With a hardness of 5.5 on the Mohs scale, charoite is well suited to being fashioned into lapidary fine art, most notably museum-quality baluster vases and goblets. *See also pp. 49 and 111.*

PIETERSITE *4x*

Farm Hopewell No. 204,
Outjo District, Kunene Region, Namibia

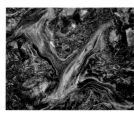

Pietersite—the brecciated form of tiger's-eye, which is in turn the pseudomorphous replacement of the asbestiform fibers of crocidolite by microcrystalline quartz—generally retains patches of the blue color of its grandparent crocidolite. In neighboring patches, the blue color is variously altered to shades of red, orange, yellow, and green. In the specimen in the photograph, there are no residual blue patches. Blue can be naturally altered to the warm end of the visible spectrum by such natural processes as activation of metal ion chromophores, oxidation, hydration, and charge transfer transitions between adjacent ferric and ferrous ions. It can also be artificially altered to deep red and reddish-brown by heating the specimen, which has the effect of oxidizing the iron. The permeation of pietersite by silica is made evident in the specimen in the photograph by the scattered milky blue and white inclusions, including the banded agate inclusion in the upper right-hand corner. *See also pp. 21, 75, 95, 105, and 149.*

CHRYSOCOLLA *6x*

Morenci Mine, Clifton-Morenci District,
Greenlee County, Arizona, USA

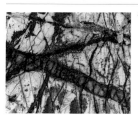

"Chrysocolla" is composed of various secondary copper minerals in varying proportions, mixed with and impregnated by variable amounts of silica. All of the colors in the specimen in the photograph are contributed by various compounds of copper that formed in the oxidation zone of the copper deposit that is exploited by the vast open pit of Morenci Mine. The bright blue coloration overprinting the big quartz vein (running subhorizontally across the middle of the photograph) and the transverse cracks is from the hydrous copper silicate, chrysocolla; the darker blue is from the hydrous copper carbonate, azurite; the green ground is from fine disseminations of the hydrous copper carbonate, malachite; the orangey-brown patches represent chalcedony colored by iron-bearing disseminations. *See also pp. 39, 43, and 67.*

LABRADORITE *3x*

Tabor Island, near Nain, Labrador,
Newfoundland and Labrador Province, Canada

Labradorite is a feldspar mineral of the plagioclase series, which has the general chemical formula, $(Ca,Na)(Si,Al)_4O_8$. At high temperatures, plagioclase feldspars form a solid solution series (within which all proportions of calcium to sodium are physically possible) between pure albite, $NaAlS_3O_8$, and pure anorthite, $CaAl_2S_2O_8$. Labradorite is arbitrarily defined as being any plagioclase feldspar with an intermediate composition of 50 to 70 percent anorthite (or, equivalently, of 50 to 70 percent albite). Labradorite is a major constituent of the world's anorthosite intrusive complexes (anorthosite being any rock composed of more than 90 percent plagioclase feldspars). The Nain Plutonic Suite, centered on the community of Nain on the northern coast of Labrador, was emplaced by recurrent magmatic pulsations over a period of 60 million years, between 1350 and 1290 million years ago. This batholithic mass contains much anorthosite, and much of it is pure labradorite. The type locality of labradorite is Pauls and Tabor Islands, nine miles offshore of Nain. Labradorite was first described by Moravian missionaries in a communication to the Reverend Benjamin Latrobe in London shortly after they established their mission station at Nain in 1771. On Tabor Island, Torngait Ujanniavingit Corporation (a subsidiary of the Labrador Inuit Development Corporation) quarries labradorite as dimension stone, attractive for its *labradorescence*—the bluish, greenish, purplish, golden yellow, and reddish-bronzy iridescent play of colors that is suggested in the photograph but which cannot be properly appreciated without movement of the actual mineral relative to the observer. Labradorescence, which is a specific instance of the optical phenomenon called *schiller*, is the result of refraction, internal reflection, and optical interference within labradorite's lamellar intergrowths when light is incident on a particular face of the labradorite crystal. The striations diagonally crossing the specimen in the photograph are perpendicular expressions of planes of *polysynthetic twinning*— across which the anorthite and albite components of the labradorite exsolved (unmixed or separated from each other as the mineral cooled) into regularly alternating, intergrown lamellae (thin parallel layers). Labradorite's exsolution lamellae appear on edge, and their labradorescence appears to best advantage, on labradorite's basal cleavage surface—as in the specimen in the photograph.

PAGE 149
PIETERSITE *4x*
Farm Hopewell No. 204,
Outjo District, Kunene Region, Namibia

Pietersite is the brecciated form of tiger's-eye, which is in turn the pseudomorphous replacement of the asbestiform fibers of crocidolite by microcrystalline quartz. The permeation of pietersite by silica is made evident in the specimen in the photograph by the microcrystalline quartz mass in the lower left-hand corner. Thanks to silica replacement, pietersite lends itself readily to cutting, carving, turning, and polishing—hence to jewelry and virtu such as cabochons, spheres, pyramids, intaglios, ashtrays, snuff bottles, and irises of eyes carved on busts. *See also pp. 21, 75, 95, 105, and 143*

PAGE 151
BOULDER OPAL *4x*
Quilpie Opal Field, Quilpie Shire,
Gregory District, Queensland, Australia

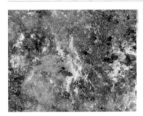

"Boulder opal" refers to opal that is dispersed through intergranular pores, cracks, and voids in siliceous ironstone concretions ("boulders") found in Queensland. In the Quilpie opal field, the boulders are discoid concretionary masses as large as 10 feet long and 4 feet wide, in the bottom of which conchoidal fractures are occasionally filled with top-grade "precious opal" (showing "play of color"). In the specimen in the photograph, the concretionary host material is represented by the salt-and-pepper background. The precious opal, which shows the full spectrum of colors, is finely dispersed and intimately bonded among the intergranular pores and voids of the siliceous ironstone. *See also pp. 25, 107, 113, and 121.*

PAGE 153
BANDED AGATE *4x*
Rio Grande do Sul, Brazil

Banded agate is an agate that is distinguished by either concentric banding or plane banding. Banded agate from Rio Grande do Sul is of the concentric variety on account of its mode of formation: in amygdules within basaltic lava flows of the Lower Cretaceous Serra Geral Formation. The central portion of the specimen in the photograph is sectioned almost parallel to the banding, so that disproportionate areas of a few bands are displayed. At the lower left of the photograph is a vug lined with drusy quartz crystals, where the amygdule failed to close. The banding of the specimen in the photograph is golden brown, lavender, blue, reddish orange, bluish gray, and pale gray. The gray hues are intrinsic pseudo-colors of chalcedony. The colored bands owe their basic coloration to chromophores such as hematite, goethite, rutile, celadonite, chlorite and chrysocolla. The color tone of each colored band, however, depends on the microstructure of the chalcedony in that band, in particular the quantity and size of the micropores. The absorbent capacity of the micropores makes chalcedony highly receptive to coloration by both natural and artificial agents. This specimen shows all-natural colors. Many Brazilian agates on the market, however, are colored with artificial stains and dyes, which are often betrayed by their specious intensity and tonelessness. Industrial coloring techniques for agates were developed in the southwest German Idar-Oberstein, Europe's industrial center for agate and jasper mining and cutting. Idar-Oberstein was flooded with cheap Brazilian agates in the mid-nineteenth century and in 1870 had to close its own mines, which had been in continuous operation since the sixteenth century. Brazilian agates dominate the world market today and will continue to do so indefinitely. The total area of the agate-bearing Paraná lavas of the Serra Geral Formation, which were extruded 132 million years ago precursory to the rifting of South America and Africa, is 470,000 square miles—equal to the area of the whole of South Africa. *See also pp. 33 and 119.*

PAGE 155
DENDRITIC AGATE *6x*
Madagascar

"Dendritic agate" is an example of an agate (a translucent chalcedony or cryptocrystalline quartz) that is not banded but is rather a variety of "moss agate" (an agate with variously splotched areas, commonly arborescent in shape). This particular specimen of "dendritic agate" from someplace in Madagascar appears to be a "hapax legomenon"—a mineral statement encountered only once in the literature. It does not readily submit to further classification. Certain observations and speculations can nevertheless be made. The trellis of acicular inclusions in the vortex of sagenitic agate that transparently encloses the tiny drusy geode at the center of the photograph suggests the presence of titanium oxide. The dendritic frill of the broad strokes of the opaque triangular enclosure around the geode is consistent with a manganese oxide and hydroxide composition. The orangey red and greenish yellow nimbus around two legs of the triangle is consistent with the chromatic effect of iron oxides and hydroxides superimposed on the bluish violet ground color. The bluish corona around the third leg is consistent with the chromatic effect of manganese oxide superimposed on the ground color, which might be attributable to amethystine color centers. The bright seam dropping down from the geode represents the final closure of the center of the crack plane, across which rough bilateral symmetry operates.

Rock Donors

An extensive collection of polished rock photographs has been made possible only by the trust and generosity of the following people who have allowed me to photograph their rocks:

Jean Pierre and Christophe Agesilas of Les Mineraux in Paris, France
Potakov Anatoli of St. Petersburg, Russia
Glenn Archer of Australian Outback Mining in Mount Helena, Western Australia, Australia
John Bennett of Australian Rough and Tumble in Perth, Western Australia, Australia
Tom Birdsall and Tina Heaney of Opalcentric in Bondville, Vermont, USA
Salim Chatta of Chatta Brothers Malachite in Montreal, Canada
Simon Cohen of Shirehampton, Bristol, Great Britain
Loy and Althea Crapo of The Bug House, Delta, Utah, USA
Ken Eisenbarth of Tyson's Fine Minerals in Edmonton, Alberta, Canada
Alex Fagotti of Prospector's Paradise in Allouez, Michigan, USA
Rod Griffin of Rod Griffin Opal in Yowah, Queensland, Australia
Andreas Guhr of Mineralien Zentrum in Hamburg, Germany
Todd Harris of The Zion Prospector in Springdale, Utah, USA
Will Honzell of House of Gems in Sparks, Nevada, USA
Dale and Sue Huett of West Coast Mining in College Place, Washington, USA
Phil and Emma Johnson of Johnson Lapidary in Sparks, Nevada, USA
Sherman and Sandra Keene of Twoesses.com in Salt Lake City, Utah, USA
Dewald and Hannes Kleynhans of Kristalle Gallerie in Swakopmund, Namibia
Thomas Lane of Lane Lapidary in Tucson, Arizona, USA
Bob and Mary Lewis of Gems Galore in Mountain View, California, USA
Yang Lianzhong of U. S. Feitian Handicrafts in Monterey Park, California, USA
Angelique Mango-pfingsten of Larimar Valley Mines in Chula Vista, California, USA
John and Karen Mediz of Copper City Rock Shop in Globe, Arizona, USA
Bruno and Marie-Claire Milani of Mineral Mania 96 in Tucson, Arizona, USA
Joseph Caruso of M&M Septarian in Kane County, Utah, USA
Eugene Mueller of The Gem Shop in Cedarburg, Wisconsin, USA
Carlos and Giovanna Oddi of La Plata, Argentina
Paul Obenich of Madagascar Minerals in Antananarivo, Madagascar
John Papajohn Jr. of JP International Mining and Colored Gemstones in Quogue, New York, USA
Jean-Louis Portafaix of ROC 3000 in Carpentras, France
Tom and Sue Robertson of Robertson's Rock Works in Salem Oregon, USA
Paul Sedawie of Seda Opals in Lightning Ridge, New South Wales, Australia
Tom Smith of Magic Mountain Gems in Cortaro, Arizona, USA
Prof. Vladimir Shevchenko of Ecogen in Moscow, Russia
Dr. Gennadiv Skublov of Russian Minerals in St. Petersburg, Russia
Lawrence and Sunni Stoller of CrystalWorks in Bend, Oregon, USA
Philip, Denise, and Michael Stone of Opalgraphics in Oxenford, Queensland, Australia
Top Gem Minerals in Tucson, Arizona, USA
TPH Lapidary in Scottsdale, Arizona, USA
V-Rock Shop in Tucson, Arizona, USA
Dr. Jacek Wachowiak of P. M. Minerwa Minerals and Gemstones in Krakow, Poland
John White of Stewartstown, Pennsylvania, USA
Roy Young and Kate Readio of Nature's Own in Boulder, Colorado, USA

Note on proprietary status:
This book includes some words which have or are asserted to have proprietary status as trademarks or otherwise. Their inclusion does not imply that they have acquired for legal purposes a non-proprietary or general significance nor any other judgment concerning their legal status.

PHOTOGRAPHER'S ACKNOWLEDGMENTS

This book would not have been possible without the encouragement and support of many dedicated friends, especially my wife and partner, Sioux Atkinson

Special thanks go to Lito Tejada-Flores for the initial book design. Subsequent design ideas were contributed by Sioux Atkinson, Robert Hutchinson, Susan Kare, Jennifer Barry, Frans Lanting, Wendover Brown, and Giraud Foster.

Thanks go to Si and Ann Frazier for sharing their mineral expertise and writing the original rock descriptions, to John White for technical reviews, and to Robert Hutchinson for his extensive research and editing of the rock descriptions. Thanks go to Lawrence Stoller for contributing a beautiful foreword which unfortunately ended up not being used, and to all of the essayists who have honored this book with their thoughtful writing. Special thanks to my daughter Laura for the closing poem. Thanks go to Robert Hutchinson, Caroline Rose, and Sioux Atkinson for their meticulous proofreading and creative editing of the text.

Thanks go to all those who reviewed the many drafts of this book—Randy and Julie Abraham, Ian Adams, Melinda Anderson, Monica Angier, Lee Ann Ashmead, Amanda Atkinson, Doris Atkinson, Laura Atkinson, Sioux Atkinson, Victoria Atkinson, Glenn Archer, Chip August, Larry Baza, Rebecca Baier, John Bennett, Daniel Benz, Roy Borrone, Marc Brown, Matt Brown, Wendover Brown, Louise Caraco, Dick Carter, Michael Chambers, Bill Colias, Bob Cook, Charles Cramer, Theresa Cretella, Brad Cross, Bill and Diana Dameron, Ulrich Dernbach, Ellen Desmond, Laird Dicker, Dona Dirlam, Barbara Dutrow, Jaimey Easler, Michael and Elizabeth Easterling, Christine Eckstrom, Lois Ertel, Marigold Fine, Giraud Foster, Thom Franklin, Bruce Fraser, Si and Ann Frazier, Robert Frey, Hans and Esther Gamma, Randy and Ann Thyme Gobbel, Estie Golan, Cal and Karith Graeber, Robert Haag, Jan Hagen, Sherry Hagen, Teri Harget, Barry Hayres, Elizabeth Henley, Andy Hertzfeld, Mac Holbert, Robert Hutchinson, Michael and Suzie Heumann, Joseph Holmes, Shunsuke Inukai, Steve Jobs, Karla Johnson, Stephen Johnson, Susan Kare, Lisa Karpinski, Ken and Janet and Lee Ann Kelly, Thomas Knoll, John Koivula, Dave and Jodie Korpi, Amala Kuster, Cara Lamb, Karl Lang, Frans Lanting, Wayne and Donna Leicht, Bob and Mary Lewis, Rosa Luna, Kevin Lynch, Mary Mac, Kathy McChesney, Ann McCormick, Pedro Meyer, Katherine and Bridger Mitchell, Catherine Mittleman, Eva Moore, Meryl Moss, Joy Mountford, Eugene Mueller, Gregory Nelson, Peter Nowell, Doug Nickel, Kirk Norlin, Pat O'Hara, Seiki Okada, Rich Pasco, Jack Passadore, Ray Pestrong, Mark Racogna, Daniel and Trudy Regan, Lloyd Rich, Beila Krow Rodin, Caroline Rose, Cheryl Royer, Vince Scarich, John Schaefer, John and Maria Schipper, Jeff Scovil, John Sculley, Satoko Sekii, Walter Shelburne, Mary Sinclitico, Rick Smolan, Alan Starr, Kathleen Steele, Margy Stein, Gene Stewart, Lawrence and Sunni Stoller, Philip and Denise Stone, Julie Taff, Jim Taskett, Lito Tejada-Flores, Bud Tribble, Wendy Turkette, Steve Upton, Jimmy Vaceck, Steve Valentine, David Vaughan, Kathy Vinson, Linde Waidhofer, Neil Waldhauer, John Warnock, Larry and Julie Weiss, Emily Wheeler, John White, Henry Wilhelm, Lara Welling, Gary Wilson, Wendell Wilson, Dan Winkler, Bana Witt, and June Culp Zeitner.

Thanks go to Mr. Inukai (President, Vanfu), Mr. Matsubara (General Manager), Mr. Oohashi (Manager), Mr. Nakano (Manager), Mr. Oohata, Mr. Anzai and the entire Vanfu team as well as Mr. Matsui (President, SunM Color), and Mr. Okada (President, iTransform Corp) for their willingness and passion to innovate and achieve a new level of excellence in printing.

Thanks go to Marc Brown, Wendover Brown, Julie Taff, and the whole BrownTrout team for their encouragement and suggestions. Special thanks go to my editor Robert Hutchinson for calming my fears and shaping this book into a beautiful work of art.

MAKING THE PHOTOGRAPHS

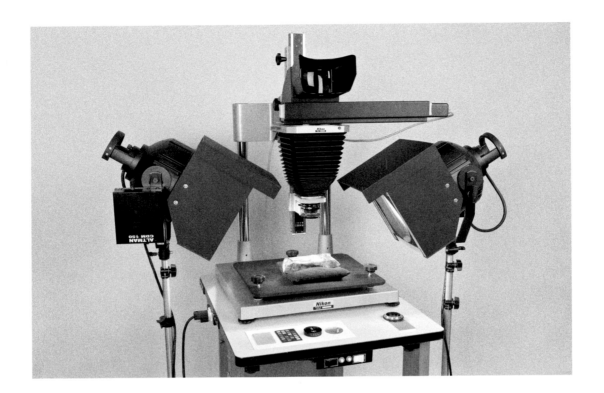

The polished rocks photographed for this book are all between one and ten inches wide. They were photographed with reflected light, using cross-polarized lighting to reduce glare, to enable seeing deeper into the rocks, and to bring out the full range of colors and textures.

Bill began photographing polished rocks in 1999, using a Hasselblad 205FCC camera, a 135mm Zeiss Makro-Planar lens mounted on the bows, Broncolor studio strobes equipped with diffusers and polarizing filters, and Fujichrome Velvia film. He scanned the resulting transparencies on a Heidelberg Tango drum scanner.

To achieve finer image detail and more accurate color, Bill now photographs polished rocks with a BetterLight Super 6K-2 large-format scanning digital camera; Altman Star Par CDM lighting fixtures equipped with heat shields, diffusers, and polarizing filters; and a 120mm Schneider Makro-Symmar HM lens mounted on a Nikon Multiphot stand, to which he has added a sliding head from a Polaroid MP4 macro system.

To exactly align the planes of the camera, the lens, and the polished stone, Bill uses a Wyler precision spirit level, a beanbag, and a plate with three leveling screws. For critical focus, he uses the digital focusing feature of the BetterLight software.

To capture colors accurately, Bill gray-balances the BetterLight camera with a digital gray card, and creates custom ICC camera profiles using a GretagMacbeth ColorChecker DC target and digital camera profiling software. To preserve these colors as he works with the photographs, Bill calibrates and makes accurate profiles for each of his computer displays and printers.

All of the photographs in this book are available as large matted and signed fine-art prints. To view a complete selection of Bill's photographs and to order prints, please visit www.billatkinson.com.

This book was created on Apple Macintosh G4 and G5 computers running the Apple Mac OS X operating system.

Both the scanned transparencies and the direct digital captures were cleaned up and refined in Adobe Photoshop, and large, fine-art prints were made with the Epson Stylus Pro 9600 printer. Smaller versions of these images were then brought into Adobe InDesign, where Bill did all the book design and layout. Lito Tejada-Flores of Western Eye Press contributed much to the initial design, and several others helped to shape the finished book. The main font used is Palatino LT Std. The first prototypes of the book were printed with the Epson Stylus Pro 9600 printer, and then many working drafts were printed with the HP Color LaserJet 9500 hdn printer.

It has been quite a challenge to reproduce the intense colors of these photographs on a four-color offset press. Most offset presses simply cannot print such a wide range of colors, and initially fewer than half of the photographs could be printed correctly. Bill worked closely with the innovative Tokyo-based printing firm, Vanfu, Inc., to dramatically improve the range of printable colors.

Numerous press runs were made to research ways to achieve higher-quality printing, such as using extra-concentrated inks, optimized ink densities, advanced screening technology, high-quality paper, and custom CMYK separations made with accurate color management. With this enhanced printing technology, Vanfu can now print all of these photographs beautifully.

The book content was delivered to Vanfu as high-resolution Adobe PDF files, and the device-independent colors were separated into high-density CMYK values using custom ICC press profiles. The Dainippon Screen's software RIP was used, with the latest Screen SPEKTA hybrid AM/FM screening technology. The printing plates were made with the Screen Plate-Rite 8600 thermal CTP platesetter using Kodak Polychrome DiamondPlate LT-3 media.

This book was printed on Vanfu's Heidelberg Speedmaster CD 102-4 sheet-fed press under the direction of master printer Katsumi Matsui. Toyo TK Hy-Unity Soy inks were used to print on extra-fine 157 gsm Oji Paper Golden Cask Dull double-sided paper and case-bound by Toppan Seihon in Tokyo.

All trademarks and registered trademarks used here are the property of their respective owners.